MEMBERS AND OFFICERS
OF THE
AMERICAN ANTIQUARIAN SOCIETY
1812–1987

Isaiah Thomas, founder and first president of the American Antiquarian Society.

Members and Officers of the American Antiquarian Society 1812–1987

WITH A LIST OF THE STAFF
DURING THE SOCIETY'S 175TH YEAR

COMPILED BY
BRADFORD F. DUNBAR

WORCESTER
AMERICAN ANTIQUARIAN SOCIETY
1987

The publication of this book was made possible
by a generous grant from
The William and Flora Hewlett Foundation
made in honor of the Society's 175th anniversary.

LIBRARY OF CONGRESS CATALOGING-IN-PUBLICATION DATA

American Antiquarian Society.
Members and officers of the
American Antiquarian Society, 1812–1987.

1. American Antiquarian Society—Registers.
2. American Antiquarian Society—Employees—Registers.
I. Dunbar, Bradford F. (Bradford Frank), 1922– .
II. Title.

E172.A3645 1987 973'.06 87-14479

ISBN 0-912296-94-1

PRINTED BY MERIDEN-STINEHOUR PRESS, LUNENBURG, VERMONT

Table of Contents

Foreword

THIS LIST OF all the members and officers of the American Antiquarian Society from 1812 to 1987 has been issued to commemorate the 175th anniversary of the Society's founding. It is the first cumulative list of AAS officers and members since the publication of the last such list forty years ago by the late Frederick L. Weis. The present pamphlet is a companion piece to another commemorative publication, *The Collections and Programs of the American Antiquarian Society: A 175th-Anniversary Guide.*

In the century and three-quarters of the Society's existence, 2,050 men and women have been elected to membership in AAS. Even in the last decade and a half of the twentieth century, AAS adheres to a policy, inherited from its early nineteenth-century origins, whereby its members elect their colleagues, although membership brings with it no special privileges of access to the Society's superb library collections or to participation in its programs. On the contrary, the Society serves, without fee, an extraordinarily broad and diverse set of constituents—professional scholars and advanced graduate students from all over the nation and the world, genealogists and local historians, Worcester-area undergraduates, and laypeople wishing to enrich themselves through lectures, concerts, and exhibitions. For those wishing to support AAS financially in a significant way, membership in the Society's friends group, the Worcester Association for Mutual Aid in Detecting Thieves, is available to anyone who gives annually to AAS a minimum of $150 in cash or in kind.

The specific rules concerning membership have changed several times since the founding in 1812; Weis provides the details up to 1947 in his pamphlet. For the first nineteen years of the Society's existence, no limit was placed on the number of members. In 1831, a limit of 140 was set, a ceiling that remained in force until 1907, when the number was increased to 175. The members voted to increase the limit to 200 in 1923. Like the ceiling on the national debt, the upper limits of AAS membership have been steadily increased to reflect both the growth and expansion of the American population and the development of those groups traditionally constituting the Society's membership. Thus the new bylaws of the Society ratified at the annual meeting in 1968 codified a 300-person limit. The raising of the limit to 400 occurred in 1975, that to 500 in 1981. A proposal to raise the limit to 600 was approved at the semiannual meeting in April 1987. Policy relating to dues and assessments has also varied over the years. Dues and assessments came and went, and came again, between 1812 and 1925. They have not been reinstituted since they were last dropped in that latter year.

Such membership by election and with no requirements of dues payments or assessments has often been characterized as honorary. Certainly, there is such an element in selection to this ancient and worthy organization, but, within the last generation at least, the extreme demands placed on the Society for its survival, prosperity, and delivery of services to scholarship have made the direct and willing support of its membership more important than ever. Today, members are elected for their contributions to the advancement of historical scholarship in America, or for their willingness to aid the cause of humanistic scholarship, but the support of all members through word, deed, or financial aid is clearly called for.

Although two other historical societies—the Massachusetts Historical Society and the New-York Historical Society—were founded before AAS, AAS is the first such institution to be national in the scope of its interests, collections, and membership. During much of its first century, in fact, the Society took the entire Western hemisphere as its field of study, and the membership rolls in the past clearly reflected that concomitant interest through the election of members from those portions of the Americas south of the Rio Grande. In all, thirty-three foreign countries are represented on the list of foreign members of AAS. Domestically, thirty-eight states and the District of Columbia appear as the place of residence for AAS members at the time of their election. Not surprisingly, given the close relationship of AAS to the City of Worcester and the Commonwealth of Massachusetts, 781 members, or about thirty-eight percent, were Massachusetts residents when elected. Of that number, 231 resided in Worcester. There are, in midsummer 1987, 497 members listed on the Society's rolls. Thus, nearly one of every four persons ever to be a member of the Society is a member now. The percentage of current members resident in Massachusetts when elected is about thirty-five percent, a bit lower than the historic percentage for 1812 to the present. The table following provides a geographical breakdown of all 2,050 members from 1812 to 1987 and of the 497 current members.

MEMBERS OF THE AMERICAN ANTIQUARIAN SOCIETY,
BY PLACE OF RESIDENCE WHEN ELECTED
1812–1987 AND MID-1987

Place	*Total Membership 1812–1987*	*Present Membership mid-1987*
Alabama	5	1
Arkansas	1	0
California	52	32
Colorado	3	2
Connecticut	96	30
Delaware	7	2
District of Columbia	78	27
Florida	3	0
Georgia	7	2
Hawaii	2	1
Illinois	32	14
Indiana	5	1

Place		*Total Membership 1812–1987*		*Present Membership mid-1987*
Iowa		6		2
Kentucky		13		0
Louisiana		14		3
Maine		34		4
Maryland		39		16
Massachusetts		781		175
Michigan		24		13
Minnesota		11		5
Mississippi		4		0
Missouri		11		3
Montana		1		0
New Hampshire		47		5
New Jersey		35		14
New Mexico		1		0
New York		211		57
North Carolina		12		7
Ohio		52		2
Oregon		4		0
Pennsylvania		94		20
Rhode Island		64		6
South Carolina		13		3
Tennessee		12		2
Texas		8		6
Vermont		15		8
Virginia		40		20
Washington		6		4
Wisconsin		14		4
	Total U.S.	1,857	Total U.S.	491
Foreign			*Foreign*	
Argentina		6		0
Belgium		1		0
Bolivia		1		0
Brazil		3		0
British Guiana		1		0
British Honduras		1		0

Canada	22		4
Central America	1		0
Chile	1		0
Columbia	1		0
Costa Rica	1		0
Cuba	2		0
Denmark	3		0
Ecuador	1		0
England	53		2
France	24		0
Germany	13		0
Greece	8		0
Honduras	1		0
India	1		0
Ireland	2		0
Italy	3		0
Jamaica	4		0
Mexico	21		0
Norway	1		0
Peru	2		0
Portugal	1		0
Russia	1		0
Scotland	6		0
Singapore	1		0
Spain	3		0
Switzerland	2		0
Turkey	1		0
Total Foreign	193	Total Foreign	6
Grand Total	2,050	Grand Total	497

The expansion of AAS membership is only partly apparent in the table, following, of the total number of members contained in previous cumulative membership lists.

1812–1836	*Transactions*, Vol. 2, 1836, pp. 565–73	302 names
1812–1839	*Proceedings*, Oct. 1839, pp. 1–16	323 names
1812–1855	*Proceedings*, Oct. 1855, pp. 39–54	408 names

1855–1868	*Proceedings*, Oct. 1868	81 names
1812–1912	*Proceedings*, Vol. 22, pp. 357–406	1,076 names
1812–1947	*Proceedings*, Vol. 56, pp. 289–333 (Weis)	1,407 names
1812–1987	The present publication	2,050 names

Absent from Weis's compilation of four decades ago are the names of any women. The late Esther Forbes, the Pulitzer-Prize-winning author of *Paul Revere and the World He Lived In*, *Johnny Tremaine*, and *A Mirror for Witches*, was the Society's first woman member, having been elected in April 1960. The first woman elected to the Council, or governing board, was Cecelia Kenyon, a Smith College political scientist, who served in that capacity from 1973 to 1979. To another Smith College academic, college president Jill Conway, went the honor (in 1985) of being the first woman vice-president of AAS. She has been nominated to succeed to the presidency in 1987.

The rest of this volume is divided into three parts. The first is a list in alphabetical order of all 2,050 members of AAS throughout history. Accompanying these members' names is the date of election to the Society, birth and death dates, and the place of residence at the time of election. Obviously, not all of these facts could be discovered. For living members, a known birth date is followed simply by a hyphen. For deceased members whose birth dates are not known the abbreviation *d.* precedes the date of death. The abbreviation *b.* precedes the birth date of members known or presumed to be deceased but for whom no date of death is available. An asterisk appears next to the names of the relatively few members who have resigned. Members for whom only the year *1812* is given under the column for date of election were the original incorporators and 'charter members' of AAS, with two exceptions. One individual, William Paine, had been omitted from the list in the establishing legislation either inadvertently or because of his Loyalist sympathies during the Revolution, but became the first person *elected* to membership, on November 19, 1812. In contrast, the name of John Lowell (1769–1840) *was* given in the list of incorporators, but was done without Lowell's consent, and Lowell never considered himself a member. Following the list of all members is a list of all the officers of the Society since 1812, arranged by office and then by date of earliest service. Following this is a list of all of the members of the Society's staff who were employed (even if only temporarily) at some time during the Society's 175th-anniversary year, that is, from October 15, 1986, to the time late in the summer of 1987 when this book went to press. Shown along with the staff members' names are the dates of their first employment at AAS and the current or last position they held.

Staff member Bradford F. Dunbar ably compiled these lists. After a career spent at Dun & Bradstreet, Mr. Dunbar retired, first to a volunteer position at AAS, then to a part-time and eventually a full-time second career here. Although the 1,407 members listed in Frederick L. Weis's 1947 compilation provided Mr. Dunbar with a solid basis for his updating, he has double-checked Weis's work and has, of course, done the necessary research in past volumes of the *Proceedings of the American Antiquarian Society*, 'Who's Whos', genealogies, and other sources to bring the listing up to the present moment.

The American Antiquarian Society is well known for the superb library collections under its care, but it has been the stewardship of the members, officers, and staff listed here, and others unnamed as well, who have breathed life into those collections and made them useful to all the American people.

John B. Hench
August 12, 1987

Members of the Society, 1812–1987

ELECTED	NAME	BIRTH AND DEATH DATES	RESIDENCE WHEN ELECTED
Apr. 1973	Aaron, Daniel	Aug. 4, 1912 –	Cambridge, Mass.
Jul. 1815	Abbot, Benjamin	Sep. 17, 1762 – Oct. 25, 1849	Exeter, N.H.
Jun. 1813	Abbot, John Lovejoy	Nov. 29, 1783 – Oct. 17, 1814	Boston, Mass.
Apr. 1985	Abbot, William Wright, III	May 20, 1922 –	Charlottesville, Va.
Oct. 1986	Abell, Millicent D.	Feb. 15, 1934 –	San Diego, Calif.
Oct. 1982	Achorn, Robert Comey	Mar. 31, 1922 –	Worcester, Mass.
Apr. 1946	Adams, Arthur	May 12, 1881 – Jun. 21, 1960	Hartford, Conn.
Oct. 1891	Adams, Charles Francis	May 27, 1835 – Mar. 20, 1915	Quincy, Mass.
Oct. 1887	Adams, Charles Kendall	Jan. 24, 1835 – Jul. 26, 1902	Ithaca, N.Y.
Oct. 1813	Adams, Ebenezer	Oct. 22, 1765 – Aug. 15, 1841	Hanover, N.H.
Oct. 1949	Adams, Frederick Baldwin, Jr.	Mar. 28, 1910 –	New York, N.Y.
Apr. 1899	Adams, George Burton	Jun. 3, 1851 – May 26, 1925	New Haven, Conn.
Oct. 1884	Adams, Henry	Feb. 16, 1838 – Mar. 27, 1918	Washington, D.C.
Apr. 1881	Adams, Herbert Baxter	Apr. 16, 1850 – Jul. 30, 1901	Baltimore, Md.
Apr. 1922	Adams, James Truslow	Oct. 16, 1878 – May 18, 1949	Bridgehampton, N.Y.
Dec. 1813	Adams, John	Oct. 19, 1735 – Jul. 4, 1826	Quincy, Mass.
Oct. 1950	Adams, John	Jul. 17, 1875 – Aug. 29, 1964	Milton, Mass.
Oct. 1839	Adams, John Quincy	Jul. 11, 1767 – Feb. 23, 1848	Quincy, Mass.
Jun. 1814	Adams, Nathaniel	1756 – Aug. 5, 1829	Portsmouth, N.H.
Oct. 1924	Adams, Randolph Greenfield	Nov. 7, 1892 – Jan. 4, 1951	Ann Arbor, Mich.
Oct. 1946	Adams, Samuel Hopkins	Jan. 26, 1871 – Nov. 16, 1958	Auburn, N.Y.
Apr. 1818	Adams, Seth	d. Sep. 8, 1853	Zanesville, Ohio
Apr. 1957	Adams, Thomas Boylston	Jul. 25, 1910 –	South Lincoln, Mass.
Apr. 1959	Adams, Thomas Randolph	May 22, 1921 –	Providence, R.I.
Oct. 1964	Adams, William Howard		Leés Summit, Mo.
Oct. 1983	Adomeit, Ruth Elizabeth	Jan. 30, 1910 –	Cleveland, Ohio
Oct. 1979	Ahlstrom, Sydney Eckman	Dec. 16, 1920 – Jul. 3, 1984	New Haven, Conn.

Oct. 1918	Aiken, Alfred Lawrence	Jul. 6, 1870 – Dec. 13, 1946	Worcester, Mass.
Oct. 1920	Aiken, John Adams	Sep. 16, 1850 – Jan. 28, 1927	Greenfield, Mass.
Oct. 1865	Alden, Ebenezer	Mar. 17, 1788 – Jan. 26, 1881	Randolph, Mass.
Apr. 1947	Alden, John	Feb. 12, 1914 –	Philadelphia, Pa.
Jul. 1815	Alden, Roger	Feb. 11, 1754 – Nov. 5, 1836	Meadville, Pa.
Jun. 1813	Alden, Timothy	Aug. 28, 1771 – Jul. 5, 1839	Elizabeth Town, N.J.
Oct. 1865	Aldrich, Peleg Emory	Aug. 2, 1813 – Mar. 14, 1895	Worcester, Mass.
Apr. 1919	Alfaro, Anastasio	d. Jan. 19, 1951	San Jose, Costa Rica
Oct. 1816	Allen, Benjamin	ca. 1771 – Jul. 20, 1836	Albany, N.Y.
Oct. 1827	Allen, Charles	Aug. 9, 1797 – Aug. 6, 1869	Worcester, Mass.
Apr. 1923	Allen, Gardner Weld	Jan. 19, 1856 – Jul. 12, 1944	Boston, Mass.
Jul. 1826	Allen, Joseph	Aug. 15, 1790 – Feb. 23, 1873	Northborough, Mass.
Apr. 1985	Allen, Sue		New Haven, Conn.
Jun. 1814	Allen, William	Jan. 2, 1784 – Jul. 16, 1868	Pittsfield, Mass.
Apr. 1888	Allen, William Francis	Sep. 5, 1830 – Dec. 9, 1889	Madison, Wis.
Apr. 1985	Allis, Frederick Scouller, Jr.	Nov. 21, 1913 –	Harwich, Mass.
Apr. 1912	Alvord, Clarence Walworth	May 21, 1868 – Jan. 25, 1928	Urbana, Ill.
Apr. 1910	Ambrosetti, Juan Bautista	d. May 28, 1917	Buenos Aires, Argentina
Apr. 1854	Ames, Ellis	Oct. 17, 1809 – Oct. 30, 1884	Canton, Mass.
Oct. 1909	Ames, Herman Vandenburg	Aug. 7, 1865 – Feb. 7, 1935	Philadelphia, Pa.
Oct. 1879	Ammidown, Holmes	Jun. 12, 1801 – Apr. 3, 1883	Southbridge, Mass.
Apr. 1858	Amory, Thomas Coffin	Oct. 16, 1813 – Aug. 20, 1889	Boston, Mass.
Oct. 1906	Amundsen, Roald	Jul. 16, 1872 – Jun., 1928	Christiania, Norway
Apr. 1880	Ancona, Eligio	Dec. 1, 1836 – Apr. 3, 1893	Merida, Yucatan
Oct. 1976	Andersen, Elmer L.	Jun. 17, 1909 –	St. Paul, Minn.
Apr. 1885	Anderson, Joseph	Dec. 16, 1836 – Aug. 18, 1916	Waterbury, Conn.
Apr. 1864	Anderson, Martin Brewer	Feb. 12, 1815 – Feb. 25, 1890	Rochester, N.Y.
Oct. 1816	Anderson, Robert	Jul. 7, 1750 – Feb. 20, 1830	Edinburgh, Scotland
Apr. 1982	Anderson, Thomas Richard	Sep. 29, 1911 –	Minneapolis, Minn.
Oct. 1907	Andrews, Charles McLean	Feb. 22, 1863 – Sep. 9, 1943	Baltimore, Md.
1812	Andrews, Ebenezer Turell	Nov. 18, 1766 – Oct. 9, 1851	Boston, Mass.
Apr. 1893	Andrews, Elisha Benjamin	Jan. 10, 1844 – Oct. 30, 1917	Providence, R.I.
Oct. 1822	Andrews, John		Chillicothe, Ohio
Jan. 1815	Andrews, Josiah Bishop	Mar. 17, 1775 – Apr. 26, 1853	New York, N.Y.
Oct. 1890	Angell, James Burrill	Jan. 7, 1829 – Apr. 1, 1916	Ann Arbor, Mich.
Apr. 1982	Appleby, Joyce Oldham	Apr. 9, 1929 –	Los Angeles, Calif.
Sep. 1813	Appleton, Jesse	Nov. 17, 1772 – Nov. 12, 1819	Brunswick, Maine

Oct. 1854	Appleton, Nathan	Oct. 6, 1779 – Jul. 14, 1861	Boston, Mass.
Oct. 1924	Appleton, William Sumner	May 29, 1874 – Nov. 24, 1947	Boston, Mass.
Apr. 1977	Appley, Mortimer Herbert	Nov. 21, 1921 –	Worcester, Mass.
May 1838	Argyropoulos, George		Athens, Greece
Oct. 1962	Armstrong, Rodney	Mar. 5, 1923 –	Exeter, N.H.
Oct. 1962	Arndt, Karl John Richard	1903 –	Worcester, Mass.
Jul. 1815	Arnold, Samuel Greene	Jan. 20, 1778 – Feb. 19, 1826	Providence, R.I.
Jul. 1815	Atherton, Charles Humphrey	Aug. 14, 1773 – Jan. 8, 1853	Amherst, N.H.
Apr. 1818	Atwater, Caleb	Dec. 25, 1778 – Mar. 13, 1867	Circleville, Ohio
Jul. 1815	Atwater, Jeremiah	Dec. 27, 1773 – Jul. 29, 1858	Carlisle, Pa.
Oct. 1924	Atwood, Wallace Walter	Oct. 1, 1872 – Jul. 24, 1949	Worcester, Mass.
Apr. 1869	Avezac-Macaya, Marie Armand Pascal D'	1799 – Jan., 1875	Paris, France
Oct. 1909	Ayer, Edward Everett	Nov. 16, 1841 – May 3, 1927	Chicago, Ill.
Oct. 1908	Ayer, James Bourne	Jan. 6, 1849 – May 14, 1910	Boston, Mass.
Oct. 1942	Ayer, Nathaniel Farwell	Jun. 24, 1879 – Jul. 26, 1948	Boston, Mass.
Apr. 1882	Ayme, Louis Henry	May 29, 1855 – May 16, 1912	Merida, Yucatan
Oct. 1946	Babb, James Tinkham, Jr.	Aug. 23, 1899 – Jul. 21, 1968	New Haven, Conn.
Apr. 1979	Babbidge, Homer Daniels, Jr.	May 18, 1925 – Mar. 27, 1984	Hartford, Conn.
Oct. 1860	Bacon, Peter Child	Nov. 11, 1804 – Feb. 7, 1886	Worcester, Mass.
Apr. 1939	Bail, Hamilton Vaughan	Feb. 3, 1892 –	North Hartland, Vt.
Oct. 1816	Bailey, John	1786 – Jun. 26, 1835	Canton, Mass.
Oct. 1960	Bailyn, Bernard	Sep. 10, 1922 –	Cambridge, Mass.
Apr. 1880	Baird, Spencer Fullerton	Feb. 3, 1823 – Aug. 19, 1887	Washington, D.C.
Apr. 1984	Bakken, Earl Elmer	Jan. 10, 1924 –	Minneapolis, Minn.
Apr. 1911	Balch, Thomas Willing	Jun. 13, 1866 – Jun. 7, 1927	Philadelphia, Pa.
Oct. 1827	Baldwin, Christopher Columbus	Aug. 1, 1800 – Aug. 20, 1835	Worcester, Mass.
Oct. 1869	Baldwin, John Denison	Sep. 28, 1809 – Jul. 8, 1883	Worcester, Mass.
Jun. 1814	Baldwin, Loammi	May 16, 1780 – Jun. 30, 1838	Cambridge, Mass.
Oct. 1893	Baldwin, Simeon Eben	Feb. 5, 1840 – Jan. 30, 1927	New Haven, Conn.
Oct. 1962	Ball, Elisabeth	Dec. 26, 1897 – Apr. 29, 1982	Muncie, Ind.
Apr. 1910	Ballivian, Manuel Vicente	Jun. 18, 1848 – Aug. 7, 1921	La Paz, Bolivia
1812	Bancroft, Aaron	Nov. 10, 1755 – Aug. 19, 1839	Worcester, Mass.
Oct. 1838	Bancroft, George	Oct. 3, 1800 – Jan. 17, 1891	Boston, Mass.
Apr. 1875	Bancroft, Hubert Howe	Mar. 5, 1832 – Mar. 2, 1918	San Francisco, Calif.
Oct. 1816	Bancroft, John Chandler	Jun. 27, 1789 – 1821	Worcester, Mass.
Apr. 1881	Bandelier, Adolph Francis	Aug. 6, 1840 – Mar. 18, 1914	Highland, Ill.
1812	Bangs, Edward	ca. 1755 – Jun. 28, 1818	Worcester, Mass.

Jan. 1819	Bangs, Edward Dillingham	Aug. 24, 1790 – Apr. 1, 1838	Worcester, Mass.
Apr. 1927	Banks, Charles Edward	Jul. 6, 1854 – Oct. 21, 1931	Martha's Vineyard, Mass.
Oct. 1978	Banks, William Nathaniel	Mar. 6, 1924 –	Temple, N.H.
Oct. 1981	Banner, James Morrill, Jr.	May 3, 1935 –	Washington, D.C.
Oct. 1935	Barbour, Thomas	Aug. 19, 1884 – Jan. 8, 1946	Boston, Mass.
Apr. 1862	Bardwell, Horatio	Nov. 3, 1788 – May 5, 1866	Oxford, Mass.
Oct. 1878	Barlee, Frederick Palgrave	Feb. 6, 1827 – Aug. 7, 1884	Belize, British Honduras
Apr. 1985	Barlow, Charles Beach	May 5, 1926 –	New Milford, Conn.
Apr. 1985	Barlow, William Pusey, Jr.	Feb. 11, 1934 –	Oakland, Calif.
Apr. 1953	Barrett, Clifton Waller	Jun. 1, 1901 –	New York, N.Y.
Apr. 1857	Barry, William	Jan. 10, 1805 – Jan. 17, 1885	Chicago, Ill.
Jan. 1819	Bartlett, Bailey	Jan. 29, 1750 – Sep. 9, 1830	Haverhill, Mass.
Apr. 1856	Bartlett, John Russell	Oct. 23, 1805 – May 28, 1886	Providence, R.I.
Oct. 1813	Bartlett, Josiah	Aug. 11, 1759 – Mar. 5, 1820	Charlestown, Mass.
Jul. 1815	Bartlett, Levi	ca. 1763 – Jan. 30, 1828	Concord, N.H.
Jun. 1814	Barton, Benjamin Smith	Feb. 10, 1766 – Dec. 19, 1815	Philadelphia, Pa.
Oct. 1878	Barton, Edmund Mills	Sep. 27, 1838 – Apr. 14, 1918	Worcester, Mass.
Oct. 1925	Barton, George Sumner	Nov. 4, 1881 – Dec. 14, 1964	Worcester, Mass.
May 1841	Barton, Ira Moore	Oct. 25, 1796 – Jul. 18, 1867	Worcester, Mass.
Jun. 1814	Barton, William	d. Jul. 22, 1823	Philadelphia, Pa.
Apr. 1854	Barton, William Sumner	Sep. 30, 1824 – Jul. 13, 1899	Worcester, Mass.
Apr. 1911	Bassett, John Spencer	Sep. 10, 1867 – Jan. 27, 1928	Northampton, Mass.
Oct. 1932	Bassler, Harvey	Apr. 21, 1883 – Mar. 14, 1950	New York, N.Y.
Oct. 1910	Bates, Albert Carlos	Mar. 12, 1865 – Mar. 27, 1954	Hartford, Conn.
Oct. 1982	Battin, Patricia Meyer	Jun. 2, 1929 –	New York, N.Y.
Apr. 1972	Bauer, Frederick Edward, Jr.	Jul. 12, 1922 –	Holden, Mass.
Apr. 1887	Baxter, James Phinney	Mar. 23, 1831 – May 8, 1921	Portland, Maine
Apr. 1933	Baxter, James Phinney, III	Feb. 15, 1893 – Jun. 17, 1975	Cambridge, Mass.
Jul. 1815	Bayard, James Asheton	Jul. 28, 1767 – Aug. 6, 1815	Wilmington, Del.
Apr. 1897	Bayard, Thomas Francis	Oct. 29, 1828 – Sep. 28, 1898	Wilmington, Del.
Jun. 1814	Baylis, William	Sep. 15, 1776 – Sep. 26, 1865	Bridgewater, Mass.
Apr. 1982	Beales, Ross Worn, Jr.	Dec. 17, 1940 –	Holden, Mass.
Oct. 1966	Beals, Philip Charles	Oct. 4, 1919 –	Southboro, Mass.
Oct. 1962	Beard, James Franklin, Jr.	Feb. 14, 1919 –	Worcester, Mass.
Apr. 1972	*Bechtel, Kenneth Karl	Jul. 4, 1904–	Kentfield, Calif.
Jan. 1815	Beck, Theodric Romeyn	Aug. 11, 1791 – Nov. 19, 1855	New York, N.Y.
Oct. 1932	Becker, Carl Lotus	Sep. 7, 1873 – Apr. 10, 1945	Ithaca, N.Y.

* resigned

Apr. 1887	Beddoe, John	Sep. 21, 1826 – Jul. 19, 1911	Bristol, England
Oct. 1972	Bedini, Silvio A.	Jan. 17, 1917 –	Washington, D.C.
Apr. 1908	Beer, William	May 1, 1849 – Feb. 1, 1927	New Orleans, La.
Oct. 1922	Belknap, Henry Wyckoff	May 18, 1860 – Sep. 19, 1946	Salem, Mass.
Apr. 1899	Bell, Alexander Graham	Mar. 3, 1847 – Aug. 2, 1922	Washington, D.C.
Oct. 1868	Bell, Charles Henry	Nov. 18, 1823 – Nov. 11, 1893	Exeter, N.H.
Apr. 1980	Bell, James Brugler	Apr. 17, 1932 –	Boston, Mass.
Apr. 1879	Bell, John James	Oct. 30, 1827 – Aug. 22, 1893	Exeter, N.H.
Oct. 1974	Bell, Walter Douglas	Jul. 24, 1921 –	Holden, Mass.
Apr. 1961	Bell, Whitfield Jenks, Jr.	Dec. 3, 1914 –	New Haven, Conn.
Oct. 1892	Bellows, John	Jan. 18, 1831 – May 5, 1902	Gloucester, England
Apr. 1925	Bemis, Frank Brewer	Oct. 15, 1861 – Mar. 10, 1935	Beverly Farms, Mass.
Oct. 1932	Bemis, Samuel Flagg	Oct. 20, 1891 – Sep. 27, 1973	Washington, D.C.
Apr. 1899	Benedict, George Grenville	Dec. 10, 1826 – Apr. 8, 1907	Montpelier, Vt.
Apr. 1977	Benedict, Joseph Targonski	Apr. 22, 1912 –	Worcester, Mass.
Apr. 1884	Benitez, Justo	Aug. 6, 1833 – Jun. 12, 1900	Mexico City, Mexico
Oct. 1984	Benjamin, Richard Dyke	May 11, 1938 –	New York, N.Y.
Oct. 1927	Benjamin, William Evarts	Feb. 19, 1859 – Feb. 24, 1940	New York, N.Y.
Dec. 1813	Benson, Egbert	Jun. 21, 1746 – Aug. 24, 1833	New York, N.Y.
Oct. 1975	Benson, Lee	Jan. 19, 1922 –	Philadelphia, Pa.
Apr. 1976	Bentinck-Smith, William	Jan. 22, 1914 –	Groton, Mass.
Feb. 1813	Bentley, William	Jun. 22, 1759 – Dec. 29, 1819	Salem, Mass.
Oct. 1855	Benton, Thomas Hart	Mar. 14, 1782 – Apr. 10, 1858	St. Louis, Mo.
Apr. 1976	Bercovitch, Sacvan	Oct. 4, 1933 –	New York, N.Y.
Oct. 1876	Berendt, Carl Hermann	Nov. 12, 1817 – Apr. 12, 1878	Merida, Yucatan
Oct. 1867	Bergenroth, Gustav Adolph	Feb. 26, 1813 – Feb. 13, 1869	London, England
Apr. 1962	Berkeley, Francis Lewis, Jr.	Apr. 9, 1911 –	Charlottesville, Va.
May 1838	Betham, William	May 22, 1779 – Oct. 26, 1853	Dublin, Ireland
Oct. 1921	Beveridge, Albert Jeremiah	Oct. 6, 1862 – Apr. 27, 1927	Indianapolis, Ind.
Apr. 1968	Biddle, James	Jul. 8, 1929 –	Washington, D.C.
Apr. 1987	Bidwell, John		Los Angeles, Calif.
Oct. 1946	Bieber, Ralph Paul	May 9, 1894 – Jul. 23, 1981	St. Louis, Mo.
Oct. 1813	*Bigelow, Abijah	Dec. 5, 1775 – Apr. 5, 1860	Leominster, Mass.
Aug. 1820	Bigelow, Andrew	May 7, 1795 – Apr. 1, 1877	Eastport, Maine
Apr. 1856	Bigelow, George Tyler	1810 – Apr. 12, 1878	Watertown, Mass.
May 1843	Bigelow, John Prescott	Aug. 25, 1797 – Jul. 4, 1872	Boston, Mass.
1812	Bigelow, Timothy	Apr. 30, 1767 – May 18, 1821	Medford, Mass.
Oct. 1813	Biglow, Abraham	ca. 1762 – Jul. 6, 1832	Cambridge, Mass.

* resigned

Dec. 1813	Biglow, William	Sep. 22, 1773 – Jan. 12, 1844	Boston, Mass.
Oct. 1851	Bigsby, Robert	1806 – Sep. 27, 1873	Asby-De-La-Zouch, England
Oct. 1964	Billias, George Athan	Jun. 26, 1919 –	Worcester, Mass.
Oct. 1899	Billings, John Shaw	April. 12, 1839 – Mar. 11, 1913	New York, N.Y.
Oct. 1965	Billington, Ray Allen	Sep. 28, 1903 – Mar. 3, 1981	San Marino, Calif.
Oct. 1909	Bingham, Hiram	Nov. 19, 1875 – Jun. 6, 1956	New Haven, Conn.
Oct. 1906	Bixby, William Keeney	Jan. 2, 1857– Oct. 29, 1931	St. Louis, Mo.
Jul. 1815	Blackburn, Gideon	Aug. 27, 1772 – Aug. 23, 1838	Nashville, Tenn.
1812	Blake, Francis	Oct. 14, 1774 – Feb. 23, 1817	Worcester, Mass.
Apr. 1900	Blake, Francis	Dec. 25, 1850 – Jan. 19, 1913	Weston, Mass.
Oct. 1859	Blake, George Smith	Mar. 5, 1802 – Jun. 24, 1871	Annapolis, Md.
Jan. 1815	Blake, John Lauris	Dec. 21, 1788 – Jul. 6, 1857	New London, Conn.
Oct. 1908	Blakeslee, George Hubbard	Aug. 27, 1871 – May 5, 1954	Worcester, Mass.
Apr. 1958	Blanck, Jacob	Nov. 10, 1906 – Dec. 23, 1974	Brookline, Mass.
May 1838	Blanding, William	Feb. 7, 1773 – Oct. 19, 1857	Philadelphia, Pa.
Apr. 1982	Blassingame, John Wesley	Mar. 23, 1940 –	New Haven, Conn.
Oct. 1892	Bliss, Eugene Frederick	Jul. 31, 1836 – Apr. 4, 1918	Cincinnati, Ohio
Apr. 1861	Bliss, Porter Cornelius	Dec. 28, 1838 – Feb. 1, 1885	New Haven, Conn.
Oct. 1985	Blitzer, Charles	Aug. 10, 1927 –	Durham, N.C.
Jun. 1814	Bloomfield, Joseph	Oct. 18, 1753 – Oct. 3, 1823	New York, N.Y.
Oct. 1984	Blumenthal, Joseph	Oct. 4, 1897 –	West Cornwall, Conn.
Jul. 1815	Blythe, James	Oct. 28, 1765 – May 20, 1842	Transylvania, Ky.
Apr. 1908	Boas, Franz	Jul. 9, 1858 – Dec. 24, 1942	New York, N.Y.
Jun. 1814	Bogert, John Griffith	d. Dec. 18, 1828	New York, N.Y.
Oct. 1980	Bok, Joan Toland	Dec. 31, 1929 –	Westboro, Mass.
Oct. 1829	Bolivar, Simon	Jul. 24, 1783 – Dec. 17, 1830	Colombia
Oct. 1918	Bolton, Charles Knowles	Nov. 14, 1867 – May 19, 1950	Boston, Mass.
Oct. 1913	Bolton, Herbert Eugene	Jul. 20, 1880 – Jan. 30, 1953	Berkeley, Calif.
Apr. 1950	Bolton, Theodore	Jan. 12, 1889 – Dec. 7, 1973	New York, N.Y.
May 1845	Bonaparte, Charles L. J. Laurent	May 24, 1803 – Jul. 29, 1857	Paris, France
Apr. 1858	Bond, Henry	Mar. 21, 1790 – May 4, 1859	Philadelphia, Pa.
Jun. 1814	Bond, William	d. Feb. 22, 1844	Dorchester, Mass.
Apr. 1965	Bond, William Henry	Aug. 14, 1915 –	Cambridge, Mass.
Apr. 1971	Boni, Albert	Oct. 21, 1892 – Jul. 30, 1981	New York, N.Y.
Apr. 1983	Boni, William Frederick	Jun. 14, 1910 –	Carmel, N.Y.
Apr. 1983	Boone, Gray Davis	Aug. 27, 1938 –	Tuscaloosa, Ala.

Oct. 1969	Boorstin, Daniel	Oct. 1, 1914 –	Washington, D.C.
Oct. 1926	Booth, George Francis	Nov. 11, 1870 – Sep. 1, 1955	Worcester, Mass.
Oct. 1978	Booth, Robert Welles	Mar. 31, 1915 –	Worcester, Mass.
Oct. 1951	Bortman, Mark	Jun. 28, 1896 – Jun. 1, 1967	Boston, Mass.
Jul. 1825	Bosworth, Joseph	1789 – May 27, 1876	Little Horwood, Bucks., England
Oct. 1985	Botein, Stephen	Dec. 20, 1941 – Jun. 24, 1986	East Lansing, Mich.
Dec. 1821	Botta, Carl Giuseppe Guglielmo	Nov. 6, 1766 – Aug. 10, 1837	Paris, France
Jun. 1814	Boudinot, Elias	May 2, 1740 – Oct. 24, 1821	Burlington, N.J.
Oct. 1814	Boudinot, Elisha	1742 – Oct. 12, 1819	Newark, N.J.
Apr. 1893	Bourinot, John George	Oct. 24, 1837 – Oct. 13, 1902	Ottawa, Ont.
Apr. 1903	Bourne, Edward Gaylord	Jun. 24, 1860 – Feb. 24, 1908	New Haven, Conn.
Apr. 1895	Boutell, Lewis Henry	Jul. 21, 1826 – Jan. 16, 1899	Evanston, Ill.
Apr. 1891	Bowditch, Charles Pickering	Sep. 30, 1842 – Jun. 1, 1921	Tamworth, N.H.
Oct. 1822	Bowdoin, James	Jul. 23, 1794 – Mar. 6, 1833	Boston, Mass.
Apr. 1904	Bowen, Clarence Winthrop	May 22, 1852 – Nov. 2, 1935	New York, N.Y.
Jun. 1814	Bowen, Jabez	Jun. 2, 1739 – May 7, 1815	Providence, R.I.
Oct. 1813	Bowen, Pardon	Mar. 22, 1757 – Oct. 25, 1826	Providence, R.I.
Apr. 1946	Bowen, Richard LeBaron	Apr. 4, 1878 – Aug. 9, 1969	Rehoboth, Mass.
Oct. 1815	Bowen, William	Mar. 8, 1746/7 – Jan. 17, 1832	Providence, R.I.
Oct. 1968	Bowers, Fredson Thayer	Apr. 25, 1905 –	Charlottesville, Va.
Apr. 1923	Bowles, Francis Tiffany	Oct. 7, 1858 – Aug. 3, 1927	Boston, Mass.
May 1834	Bowring, John	Oct. 17, 1792 – Nov. 23, 1872	London, England
Apr. 1936	Boyd, Julian Parks	Nov. 3, 1903 – May 28, 1980	Philadelphia, Pa.
Oct. 1984	Boyer, Paul Samuel	Aug. 2, 1935 –	Madison, Wis.
Oct. 1819	Boylston, Ward Nicholas	Nov. 22, 1749 – Jan. 7, 1828	Princeton, Mass.
Jun. 1814	Bozman, John Leeds	Aug. 25, 1757 – Apr. 20, 1823	Baltimore, Md.
Apr. 1818	Brackenridge, Henry Marie	May 11, 1786 – Jan. 18, 1871	Washington, D.C.
Jul. 1825	Bracket, Adino Nye	d. Jan. 25, 1847	Lancaster, N.H.
Apr. 1975	Brademas, John	Mar. 2, 1927 –	Washington, D.C.
Jan. 1819	Bradley, Samuel Ayer	Nov. 22, 1774-Sep. 23, 1844	Fryeburg, Maine
Apr. 1942	Brainard, Morgan Bulkeley	Jan. 8, 1879 – Aug. 28, 1957	Hartford, Conn.
Oct. 1955	Brainard, Newton Case	Dec. 26, 1880 – Jul. 16, 1964	Hartford, Conn.
May 1839	Brandis, Christian August	1790 – Jul. 24, 1867	Bonne, Switzerland
Apr. 1934	Brasch, Frederick Edward	Dec. 18, 1875 – Oct. 26, 1967	Washington, D.C.
Dec. 1813	Bray, Oliver	Apr. 2, 1776 – Dec. 26, 1823	Portland, Maine
Jan. 1819	Brazer, John	Sep. 21, 1789 – Feb. 25, 1846	Cambridge, Mass.

Oct. 1868	Brevoort, James Carson	Jul. 10, 1818 – Dec. 7, 1887	Brooklyn, N.Y.
Oct. 1965	Brew, John Otis	Mar. 28, 1906 –	Cambridge, Mass.
Apr. 1967	Brewington, Marion Vernon	Jun. 23, 1902 – Dec. 8, 1974	Sharon, Mass.
Oct. 1816	Brewster, David	Dec. 11, 1781 – Feb. 10, 1868	Edinburgh, Scotland
Oct. 1945	Bridenbaugh, Carl	Aug. 10, 1903 –	Williamsburg, Va.
Oct. 1813	Bridgham, Samuel Willard	1774 – Dec. 28, 1840	Providence, R.I.
Apr. 1977	Briel, Karl Lombard	Nov. 5, 1919 –	Millbury, Mass.
Oct. 1905	Brigham, Clarence Saunders	Aug. 5, 1877 – Aug. 13, 1963	Providence, R.I.
Oct. 1813	Brigham, Elijah	Jul. 7, 1751 – Feb. 22, 1816	Westboro, Mass.
Oct. 1846	Brinley, George	May 15, 1817 – May 16, 1875	Hartford, Conn.
Apr. 1880	Brinley, George Putnam	Apr. 10, 1842 – Aug. 24, 1892	Hartford, Conn.
Oct. 1870	Brinton, Daniel Garrison	May 13, 1837 – Jul. 31, 1899	Philadelphia, Pa.
Oct. 1957	Bristol, Roger Pattrell	Jul. 15, 1903 – Nov. 3, 1974	Charlottesville, Va.
Apr. 1986	Britton, Allen Perdue	May 25, 1914 –	Ann Arbor, Mich.
Oct. 1877	Brock, Robert Alonzo	Mar. 9, 1839 – Jul. 12, 1914	Richmond, Va.
Oct. 1975	Broderick, John Caruthers	Sep. 6, 1926 –	Rockville, Md.
Jul. 1815	Bronson, Enos	Mar. 31, 1774 – Apr. 17, 1823	Philadelphia, Pa.
Oct. 1900	Brooks, James Willson	Aug. 7, 1833 – Sep. 20, 1912	Petersham, Mass.
Oct. 1979	Brooks, John Edward	Jul. 13, 1923 –	Worcester, Mass.
Apr. 1818	Brown, Ethan Allen	Jul. 4, 1766 – Feb. 24, 1852	Cincinnati, Ohio
Oct. 1813	Brown, Francis	Jan. 11, 1784 – Jul. 27, 1820	North Yarmouth, Mass.
Oct. 1814	Brown, James	Sep. 11, 1766 – Apr. 7, 1835	New Orleans, La.
Oct. 1855	Brown, John Carter	Aug. 28, 1797 – Jun. 10, 1874	Providence, R.I.
Oct. 1888	Brown, John Nicholas	Dec. 17, 1861 – May 1, 1900	Providence, R.I.
Oct. 1947	Brown, John Nicholas	Feb. 21, 1900 – Oct. 9, 1979	Newport, R.I.
Apr. 1986	Brown, Mary Elizabeth	Aug. 15, 1913 –	Worcester, Mass.
Jul. 1815	Brown, Matthew	1776 – Jul. 29, 1853	Washington, Pa.
Jul. 1815	Brown, Moses	Sep. 12, 1738 – Sep. 7, 1836	Providence, R.I.
Oct. 1813	Brown, Nicholas	Apr. 4, 1769 – Sep. 27, 1841	Providence, R.I.
Apr. 1981	Brown, Richard David	Oct. 31, 1939 –	Storrs, Conn.
Oct. 1816	Brown, Thomas	Jan. 9, 1778 – Apr. 2, 1820	Edinburgh, Scotland
Dec. 1821	Brunton, Alexander	1772 – Feb. 9, 1854	Edinburgh, Scotland
Oct. 1925	Bryan, John Stewart	Oct. 23, 1871 – Oct. 16, 1944	Richmond, Va.
Oct. 1965	Bryant, Douglas Wallace	Jun. 20, 1913 –	Lexington, Mass.
Apr. 1882	Bryce, James	May 10, 1838 – Jan. 22, 1922	Oxford, England
Oct. 1898	Brymner, Douglas	Jul. 3, 1823 – Jun. 19, 1902	Ottawa, Ont.
Apr. 1955	Buck, Paul Herman	Aug. 25, 1899 – Dec. 23, 1978	Cambridge, Mass.
Oct. 1916	Buck, Solon Justus	Aug. 16, 1884 – May 25, 1962	Minneapolis, Minn.

Oct. 1966	Buhler, Kathryn Clark	Aug. 29, 1901 – Nov. 7, 1986	Brookline, Mass.
Oct. 1924	Bullen, Henry Lewis	Sep. 18, 1857 – Apr. 27, 1938	Jersey City, N.J.
Apr. 1855	Bullock, Alexander Hamilton	Mar. 2, 1816 – Jan. 17, 1882	Worcester, Mass.
Oct. 1937	Bullock, Alexander Hamilton	Nov. 7, 1874 – Oct. 12, 1962	Worcester, Mass.
Apr. 1888	Bullock, Augustus George	Jun. 2, 1847 – Jun. 22, 1926	Worcester, Mass.
Oct. 1952	Bullock, Augustus George	Feb. 10, 1909 –	Worcester, Mass.
Oct. 1921	Bullock, Chandler	Aug. 24, 1872 – Mar. 23, 1962	Worcester, Mass.
Apr. 1984	Bullock, John Richard	Mar. 2, 1923 –	Shrewsbury, Mass.
Apr. 1971	Burkhardt, Frederick Henry	Sep. 13, 1912 –	New York, N.Y.
Jul. 1815	Burnet, Jacob	Feb. 22, 1770 – May 10, 1853	Cincinnati, Ohio
1812	Burnside, Samuel MacGregor	Jul. 18, 1783 – Jul. 25, 1850	Worcester, Mass.
Apr. 1908	Burr, George Lincoln	Jan. 30, 1857 – Jun. 27, 1938	Ithaca, N.Y.
Jun. 1814	Burr, Jonathan	d. Aug. 2, 1842	Sandwich, Mass.
Jul. 1815	Burrill, James	Apr. 25, 1772 – Dec. 25, 1820	Providence, R.I.
Oct. 1907	Burton, Clarence Monroe	Nov. 18, 1853 – Oct. 23, 1932	Detroit, Mich.
Oct. 1870	Buschman, Karl Edward	Feb. 14, 1805 – Apr. 21, 1880	Berlin, Germany
Oct. 1981	Bushman, Richard Lyman	Jun. 20, 1931 –	Newark, Del.
Apr. 1854	Butler, James Davie	Mar. 15, 1815 – Nov. 20, 1905	Cincinnati, Ohio
Apr. 1951	Butterfield, Lyman Henry	Aug. 8, 1909 – Apr. 25, 1982	Princeton, N.J.
Apr. 1960	Butterfield, Roger Place	Jul. 29, 1907 – Jan. 31, 1981	New York, N.Y.
Oct. 1888	*Cable, George Washington	Oct. 12, 1844 – Jan. 31, 1925	Northampton, Mass.
Apr. 1986	Cabot, Jr., Harold	Sep. 4, 1929 –	Princeton, Mass.
Apr. 1925	Cabot, William Brooks	Feb. 2, 1858 – Jan. 31, 1949	Boston, Mass.
Apr. 1940	Cadbury, Henry Joel	Dec. 1, 1883 – Oct. 7, 1974	Cambridge, Mass.
Oct. 1974	Cady, Edwin Harrison	Nov. 9, 1917 –	Hillsborough, N.C.
Jul. 1815	Caldwell, Charles	May 14, 1772 – Jul. 9, 1853	Philadelphia, Pa.
Oct. 1954	*Cameron, Kenneth Walter	Oct. 12, 1908-	Hartford, Conn.
Oct. 1869	Campbell, George Douglas	Apr. 30, 1823 – Apr. 23, 1900	London, England
Apr. 1866	Campbell, James Butler	Oct. 27, 1808 – Nov. 8, 1883	Charleston, S.C.
Oct. 1877	Campbell, James Valentine	Feb. 25, 1823 – Mar. 26, 1890	Detroit, Mich.
Apr. 1946	Campbell, Le Roy Archer	Sep. 2, 1902 –	Worcester, Mass.
Apr. 1964	Campbell, Louisa Dresser	Oct. 25, 1907 –	Worcester, Mass.
Apr. 1878	Canton, Rodulfo Gregorio	d. Jul. 29, 1909	Merida, Yucatan
Apr. 1952	Cappon, Lester Jesse	Sep. 18, 1900 – Aug. 24, 1981	Williamsburg, Va.
Jul. 1815	Carey, Matthew	Jan. 28, 1760 – Sep. 16, 1839	Philadelphia, Pa.

* resigned

Apr. 1980	Carpenter, Kenneth Edward	Nov. 13, 1936 –	Newton, Mass.
Oct. 1955	Carpenter, Ralph Emerson, Jr.	Oct. 6, 1909 –	New York, N.Y.
Oct. 1886	Carr, Lucien	Dec. 15, 1829 – Jan. 27, 1915	Cambridge, Mass.
Jul. 1815	Carroll, Charles	Sep. 19, 1737 – Nov. 14, 1832	Carrollton, Md.
Jul. 1815	Carroll, John	Jan. 8, 1735 – Dec. 3, 1815	Baltimore, Md.
Apr. 1924	Carson, Hampton Lawrence	Feb. 21, 1852 – Jul. 18, 1929	Philadelphia, Pa.
Apr. 1947	Carson, Joseph	Jul. 2, 1883 – Aug. 23, 1953	Bryn Mawr, Pa.
Oct. 1977	Carter, Joseph Ray	Oct. 8, 1918 –	Worcester, Mass.
Jul. 1815	Carthy, Daniel	d. Aug. 15, 1829	Newbern, N.C.
Jun. 1813	Cary, Samuel	Nov. 24, 1785 – Oct. 23, 1815	Boston, Mass.
Oct. 1904	Casares, David	Jul. 3, 1835 – Dec. 5, 1914	Merida, Yucatan
Dec. 1821	Cass, Lewis	Oct. 9, 1782 – Jun. 17, 1866	Detroit, Mich.
Oct. 1924	Cathcart, Wallace Hugh	Apr. 2, 1865 – Sep. 6, 1942	Cleveland, Ohio
Oct. 1908	Catterall, Ralph Charles Henry	Mar. 29, 1866 – Aug. 2, 1914	Ithaca, N.Y.
Oct. 1969	Catton, Bruce	Oct. 9, 1899 – Aug. 28, 1978	New York, N.Y.
Oct. 1945	Caulfield, Ernest	Sep. 8, 1893 – May 16, 1972	Hartford, Conn.
Oct. 1902	Chamberlain, Alexander Francis	Jan. 12, 1865 – Apr. 8, 1914	Worcester, Mass.
Oct. 1815	Chamberlain, John Curtis	Jun. 5, 1772 – Dec. 8, 1834	Charlestown, N.H.
Jun. 1814	Champlin, Christopher Grant	Apr. 12, 1768 – Mar. 18, 1840	Newport, R.I.
Apr. 1978	Chandler, Alfred Du Pont, Jr.	Sep. 15, 1918 –	Cambridge, Mass.
Oct. 1857	Chandler, George	Apr. 28, 1806 – May 17, 1893	Worcester, Mass.
Oct. 1984	Chandler, Otis	Nov. 23, 1927 –	Los Angeles, Calif.
May 1843	Chandler, Peleg Whitman	Apr. 13, 1816 – May 28, 1889	Boston, Mass.
Oct. 1885	Channing, Edward	Jun. 15, 1856 – Jan. 7, 1931	Cambridge, Mass.
Apr. 1853	Chapin, Henry	May 13, 1811 – Oct. 13, 1878	Worcester, Mass.
Apr. 1914	Chapin, Howard Millar	May 11, 1887 – Sep. 17, 1940	Providence, R.I.
Apr. 1880	Chase, Charles Augustus	Sep. 9, 1833 – Jun. 5, 1911	Worcester, Mass.
Apr. 1863	Chase, Pliny Earle	Aug. 18, 1820 – Dec. 17, 1886	Philadelphia, Pa.
Oct. 1887	Chase, Thomas	Jun. 16, 1827 – Oct. 5, 1892	Providence, R.I.
Oct. 1816	Chateaubriand, François Rene August	Sep. 14, 1768 – Jul. 4, 1848	Paris, France
Apr. 1881	Chavero, Alfredo	Feb. 1, 1841 – Oct. 24, 1906	Mexico City, Mexico
Jun. 1814	Chester, John	Aug. 17, 1785 – Jan. 12, 1829	Hudson, N.Y.

Oct. 1882	Chevalier, Edouard		Paris, France
Oct. 1814	Cheves, Langdon	Sep. 17, 1776 – Jun. 26, 1857	Charleston, S.C.
Apr. 1872	Childs, George William	May 12, 1829 – Feb. 3, 1894	Philadelphia, Pa.
Apr. 1941	Chinard, Gilbert	Oct. 17, 1881 – Feb. 8, 1972	Princeton, N.J.
Oct. 1901	Church, Arthur Herbert	Jun. 2, 1834 – Jun. 1, 1915	Kew Gardens, England
Oct. 1822	Clap, Elisha	Dec. 29, 1775 – Oct. 22, 1830	Boston, Mass.
Oct. 1942	Clapham, Alfred William	May 27, 1883 – Oct. 26, 1950	London, England
Oct. 1956	Clapp, Verner Warren	Jun. 3, 1901 – Jun. 15, 1972	Washington, D.C.
Jun. 1814	Clark, Abraham	Oct., 1767 – Jul. 28, 1854	Newark, N.J.
Apr. 1974	Clark, Charles Elliot Frazer, Jr.		Bloomfield Hills, Mich.
Oct. 1974	Clark, Peter Bruce	Oct. 23, 1928 –	Detroit, Mich.
Oct. 1814	Clark, William	Aug. 1, 1770 – Sep. 1, 1838	St. Louis, Mo.
Oct. 1933	Clark, William Irving	Apr. 12, 1879 – Apr. 5, 1958	Worcester, Mass.
Oct. 1816	Clarke, Adam	ca. 1762 – Aug. 26, 1832	Millbrook, England
Oct. 1935	Clarke, Hermann Frederick	Mar. 29, 1882 – Oct. 29, 1947	Boston, Mass.
Apr. 1871	Clarke, Robert	May 1, 1829 – Aug. 26, 1899	Cincinnati, Ohio
Oct. 1820	Clay, Henry	Apr. 12, 1777 – Jun. 29, 1852	Lexington, Ky.
Oct. 1916	Clements, William Lawrence	Apr. 1, 1861 – Nov. 6, 1934	Bay City, Mich.
Oct. 1819	Clifford, John D.	ca. 1778 – May 8, 1820	Lexington, Ky.
Apr. 1870	Clifford, John Henry	Jan. 16, 1809 – Jan. 2, 1876	New Bedford, Mass.
Jun. 1814	Clinton, DeWitt	Mar. 2, 1769 – Feb. 11, 1828	New York, N.Y.
Oct. 1816	Clowes, Timothy	Mar. 18, 1787 – Jul. 16, 1847	Albany, N.Y.
Oct. 1940	Cluverius, Wat Tyler	Dec. 25, 1874 – Oct. 28, 1952	Worcester, Mass.
Jun. 1814	Cobb, David	Sep. 14, 1748 – Apr. 17, 1830	Gouldsborough, Maine
Oct. 1937	Codman, Ogden	Jan. 19, 1863 – Jan. 8, 1951	Paris, France
Jan. 1815	Codman, Stephen	Dec. 4, 1758 – May 7, 1844	Boston, Mass.
Apr. 1948	Coe, William Robertson	Jun. 8, 1869 – Mar. 14, 1955	New York, N.Y.
Jun. 1814	Coffin, Charles	Aug. 15, 1775 – Jun. 3, 1853	Greenville, Tenn.
Oct. 1931	Coffin, Howard Earle	Sep. 6, 1873 – Nov. 21, 1937	Sapeloe Island, Ga.
Oct. 1842	Cogswell, William	Jun. 5, 1787 – Apr. 18, 1850	Hanover, N.H.
Oct. 1950	Cohen, I Bernard	Mar. 1, 1914 –	Cambridge, Mass.
Apr. 1951	Cole, Arthur Harrison	Nov. 21, 1889 – Nov. 10, 1974	Cambridge, Mass.
Oct. 1947	Cole, Edward Harold	Aug. 29, 1892 – Aug. 11, 1966	Newtonville, Mass.
Oct. 1918	Cole, George Watson	Sep. 6, 1850 – Oct. 10, 1939	New York, N.Y.
Oct. 1985	Cole, John Young	Jul. 30, 1940 –	Chevy Chase, Md.

Oct. 1952	*Coleman, John Winston, Jr.	Nov. 5, 1898 –	Lexington, Ky.
Jul. 1815	Coleman, William	Feb. 14, 1766 – Jul. 13, 1829	New York, N.Y.
Oct. 1985	Coleman, William Robert	Aug. 29, 1916 –	San Bernadino, Calif.
Oct. 1950	Colt, Harris Dunscombe	Jan. 29, 1901 – Nov. 8, 1973	New York, N.Y.
Jul. 1815	Colt, Judah	d. Oct. 11, 1832	Erie, Pa.
Apr. 1885	Colton, Reuben	Nov. 27, 1855 – Feb. 26, 1936	Worcester, Mass.
Apr. 1940	Commager, Henry Steele	Oct. 25, 1902 –	New York, N.Y.
Apr. 1818	Conant, Calvin	d. Jan. 26, 1829	Putnam, Ohio
Apr. 1909	Conant, Samuel Morris	Dec. 8, 1861 – Mar. 16, 1930	Pawtucket, R.I.
Apr. 1980	Conger, Clement Ellis	Oct. 15, 1912 –	Alexandria, Va.
Oct. 1919	Connor, Robert Digges Wimberly	Sep. 26, 1878 – Feb. 25, 1950	Raleigh, N.C.
Apr. 1893	Conrad, Johannes Ernst	Feb. 28, 1839 – Apr. 25, 1915	Wittenberg, Germany
Oct. 1930	Conway, George Robert Graham	Apr. 28, 1873 – May 20, 1951	Mexico City, Mexico
Oct. 1977	Conway, Jill Kathryn Ker	Oct. 9, 1934 –	Northampton, Mass.
Apr. 1949	Cook, Philip Howard	Feb. 2, 1878 – Mar. 25, 1954	Worcester, Mass.
Oct. 1981	Cook, Stanton Rufus	Jul. 3, 1925 –	Chicago, Ill.
Apr. 1911	Coolidge, Archibald Cary	Mar. 6, 1866 – Jan. 14, 1928	Boston, Mass.
Oct. 1925	Coolidge, Calvin	Jul. 4, 1872 – Jan. 5, 1933	Washington, D.C.
May 1835	Cooper, Charles Purton	1793 – Mar. 26, 1873	London, England
Apr. 1972	Cooper, Paul Fenimore, Jr.	Mar. 3, 1930 –	Cooperstown, N.Y.
Oct. 1970	Copeland, Lammot du Pont	May 19, 1905 – Jul. 1, 1983	Wilmington, Del.
Oct. 1985	Coquillette, Daniel Robert	May 23, 1944 –	Cambridge, Mass.
Oct. 1920	Corbacho, Jorge M.	d. Mar. 16, 1947	Lima, Peru
Apr. 1905	Corey, Deloraine Pendre	Sep. 4, 1836 – May 6, 1910	Malden, Mass.
Oct. 1934	Corning, Howard	Jun. 28, 1867 – Feb. 3, 1956	Salem, Mass.
Oct. 1985	Cotsen, Lloyd Edward	Feb. 25, 1929 –	Los Angeles, Calif.
Apr. 1983	Cott, Nancy Falik	Nov. 8, 1945 –	New Haven, Conn.
Jun. 1814	Cotton, Rosseter	ca. 1758 – Aug. 12, 1837	Plymouth, Mass.
Oct. 1975	Couper, Richard Watrous	Dec. 16, 1922 –	Chappaqua, N.Y.
Oct. 1986	Cowdrey, Albert E.	Dec. 8, 1933 –	Washington, D.C.
Oct. 1847	Craig, Neville B.	Mar. 29, 1787 – Mar. 5, 1863	Pittsburgh, Pa.
Apr. 1818	Cranch, John	Oct. 12, 1751 – Jan. 23, 1821	Bath, England
Dec. 1813	Cranch, William	Jul. 17, 1769 – Sep. 1, 1855	Washington, D.C.

* resigned

Oct. 1970	Craven, Wesley Frank	May 19, 1905 – Feb. 10, 1981	Princeton, N.J.
Apr. 1975	Crawford, Richard Arthur	May 12, 1935 –	Ann Arbor, Mich.
Apr. 1897	Creighton, Mandell	Jul. 5, 1843 – Jan. 14, 1901	London, England
Apr. 1974	Cremin, Lawrence Arthur	Oct. 31, 1925 –	New York, N.Y.
Oct. 1928	Crompton, George	Jun. 7, 1872 – Nov. 16, 1953	Worcester, Mass.
Apr. 1977	Cronkite, Walter Leland, Jr.	Nov. 4, 1916 –	New York, N.Y.
Oct. 1878	Cross, William	Nov. 23, 1822 – Feb. 14, 1880	Worcester, Mass.
Oct. 1984	Crowley, Edward Denis	Jun. 19, 1926 –	Wellesley, Mass.
Apr. 1925	Cuevas, Mariano	ca. 1879 – Mar. 31, 1949	Mexico City, Mexico
Jul. 1815	Culbertson, James	Oct. 23, 1785 – Feb. 23, 1847	Zanesville, Ohio
Oct. 1814	Cumming, John Noble	d. Jul. 6, 1821	Newark, N.J.
Apr. 1972	Cummings, Abbott Lowell	Mar. 14, 1923 –	Boston, Mass.
Apr. 1912	Cundall, Frank	d. Nov. 15, 1937	Kingston, Jamaica
Oct. 1909	Cunningham, Henry Winchester	Mar. 26, 1860 – Oct. 27, 1930	Manchester, Mass.
Apr. 1979	Cunningham, Noble E., Jr.	Jul. 25, 1926 –	Columbia, Mo.
Oct. 1942	Currier, Thomas Franklin	Feb. 26, 1873 – Sep. 14, 1946	Belmont, Mass.
Oct. 1978	Curti, Merle Eugene	Sep. 15, 1897 –	Madison, Wis.
Apr. 1963	Curtis, John Whitin	Sep. 30, 1911 –	Worcester, Mass.
Oct. 1891	Curtius, Ernst	Sep. 2, 1814 – Jul. 11, 1896	Berlin, Germany
Oct. 1974	Cushing, John Daniel	Aug. 26, 1922 – Sep. 16, 1987	Hingham, Mass.
Oct. 1862	Cushman, Henry Wyles	ca. 1804 – Nov. 20, 1863	Bernardston, Mass.
Oct. 1855	Cushman, John Franklin		Oxford, Miss.
Apr. 1974	Cushman, Robert	Apr. 29, 1916 –	Worcester, Mass.
Jul. 1815	Custis, George Washington Parke	Apr. 30, 1781 – Oct. 10, 1857	Arlington, D.C.
Oct. 1822	Cuthbert, James		Berthier, Que.
Apr. 1943	Cutler, Carl Custer	ca. 1879 – Feb. 20, 1966	Mystic, Conn.
Apr. 1885	Cutler, Ebenezer	Aug. 21, 1822 – Jan. 16, 1898	Worcester, Mass.
Dec. 1813	Cutler, Manasseh	May 13, 1742 – Jul. 28, 1823	Hamilton, Mass.
Jul. 1815	Daggett, David	Dec. 31, 1764 – Apr. 12, 1851	New Haven, Conn.
Oct. 1869	Damon, Samuel Chenery	Feb. 15, 1815 – Feb. 7, 1885	Honolulu, Hawaii
Oct. 1943	Damon, Samuel Foster	Feb. 22, 1893 – Dec. 25, 1971	Providence, R.I.
Oct. 1937	Damon, Theron Johnson	Feb. 25, 1883 – Apr. 25, 1973	Concord, Mass.
Oct. 1814	Dana, Samuel Whittlesey	Feb. 13, 1760 – Jul. 21, 1830	Middletown, Conn.
Oct. 1816	Dane, Nathan	Dec. 29, 1752 – Feb. 15, 1835	Beverly, Mass.
Oct. 1971	Dangerfield, George Bubb	Oct. 28, 1904 – Oct. 27, 1986	Santa Barbara, Calif.
Oct. 1968	Daniels, Bruce Goddard	Mar. 9, 1925 –	Lincoln, Mass.
Oct. 1956	Daniels, Fred Harold	Sep. 9, 1887 – Jun. 15, 1967	Worcester, Mass.

Oct. 1980	Dann, John Christie	May 3, 1944 –	Ann Arbor, Mich.
Apr. 1983	Darnton, Robert Choate	May 10, 1939 –	Princeton, N.J.
Apr. 1960	Davidson, Alexander, Jr.	Jun. 26, 1910 – May 13, 1967	New York, N.Y.
Apr. 1987	Davidson, Cathy N.		East Lansing, Mich.
Apr. 1940	Davie, Preston	Jan. 31, 1881 – May 21, 1967	New York, N.Y.
Oct. 1813	Davis, Aaron	d. Mar. 23, 1817	Roxbury, Mass.
Apr. 1882	Davis, Andrew McFarland	Dec. 30, 1833 – Mar. 29, 1920	San Francisco, Calif.
Oct. 1982	Davis, Archibald Kimbrough	Jan. 22, 1911 –	Winston-Salem, N.C.
Oct. 1894	Davis, Cushman Kellogg	Jun. 16, 1838 – Nov. 27, 1900	St. Paul, Minn.
Apr. 1975	Davis, David Brion	Feb. 16, 1927 –	Orange, Conn.
Oct. 1867	Davis, Edward Livingston	Apr. 22, 1834 – Mar. 2, 1912	Worcester, Mass.
Apr. 1858	Davis, Edwin Hamilton	Jan. 22, 1811 – Jan. 15, 1888	New York, N.Y.
Apr. 1862	Davis, Horace	Mar. 16, 1831 – Jul. 12, 1916	San Francisco, Calif.
May 1841	Davis, Isaac	Jun. 2, 1799 – Apr. 1, 1883	Worcester, Mass.
Feb. 1813	Davis, John	Jan. 25, 1761 – Jan. 14, 1847	Boston, Mass.
Jun. 1821	Davis, John	Jan. 13, 1787 – Apr. 19, 1854	Worcester, Mass.
Apr. 1851	Davis, John Chandler Bancroft	Dec. 29, 1822 – Dec. 27, 1907	Worcester, Mass.
Apr. 1912	Davis, Livingston	Aug. 13, 1882 – Jan. 11, 1932	Boston, Mass.
Apr. 1973	Davis, Richard Beale	Jun. 3, 1907 – Mar. 30, 1981	Knoxville, Mass.
Oct. 1978	Davis, Shelby Cullom	Apr. 1, 1909 –	New York, N.Y.
Oct. 1950	Davis, Walter Goodman	May 14, 1885 – Jul. 11, 1966	Portland, Maine
Oct. 1963	Davis, Warren Gilbert	Dec. 19, 1887 – Aug. 2, 1985	Worcester, Mass.
Oct. 1979	Davis, William Curtis Carroll	Feb. 18, 1916 –	Baltimore, Md.
Oct. 1889	Deady, Matthew Paul	May 12, 1824 – Mar. 24, 1893	Portland, Ore.
Oct. 1851	Deane, Charles	Nov. 10, 1813 – Nov. 13, 1889	Cambridge, Mass.
Oct. 1816	Dearborn, Henry	Feb. 23, 1751 – Jun. 6, 1829	Boston, Mass.
Oct. 1815	Dearborn, Henry Alexander Scammell	Mar. 3, 1783-Jul. 29, 1851	Boston, Mass.
Oct. 1962	Dechert, Robert	Nov. 29, 1895 – Nov. 8, 1975	King of Prussia, Pa.
Apr. 1931	Deering, Frank Cutter	Jan. 28, 1866 – Aug. 12, 1939	Saco, Maine
Apr. 1974	Degler, Carl Neumann	Feb. 6, 1921 –	Stanford, Calif.
Apr. 1969	De Golyer, Everett Lee, Jr.	d. Dec. 17, 1977	Dallas, Tex.
Oct. 1922	De La Torre, Carlos	d. Feb. 19, 1950	Havana, Cuba
Apr. 1979	Demos, John Putnam	May 2, 1937 –	Waltham, Mass.
Apr. 1917	De Puy, Henry Farr	Apr. 12, 1859 – Oct. 14, 1924	New York, N.Y.
Apr. 1987	Deranian, Hagop Martin	Aug. 21, 1922 –	Shrewsbury, Mass.

Sep. 1813	Derby, Elias Hasket	Jan. 10, 1766 – Sep. 16, 1826	Salem, Mass.
Oct. 1871	Desor, Edward	Feb. 11, 1811 – Feb. 23, 1882	Neufchatel, Switzerland
Oct. 1878	Devens, Charles	Apr. 4, 1820 – Jan. 7, 1891	Worcester, Mass.
Oct. 1945	De Voto, Bernard Augustine	Jan. 11, 1897 – Nov. 14, 1955	Cambridge, Mass.
Oct. 1869	Dewey, Francis Henshaw	Jul. 12, 1821 – Dec. 24, 1887	Worcester, Mass.
Oct. 1891	Dewey, Francis Henshaw	Mar. 23, 1856 – Apr. 20, 1933	Worcester, Mass.
Apr. 1936	Dewey, Francis Henshaw, Jr.	May 19, 1887 – Nov. 16, 1974	Worcester, Mass.
Apr. 1981	Dewey, Francis Henshaw, III	Feb. 4, 1919 –	Holden, Mass.
Apr. 1966	Dewey, Henry Bowen	Apr. 15, 1924 –	Worcester, Mass.
Apr. 1879	Dexter, Franklin Bowditch	Sep. 11, 1842 – Aug. 13, 1920	New Haven, Conn.
Apr. 1876	Dexter, George	Jul. 18, 1838 – Dec. 18, 1883	Cambridge, Mass.
Apr. 1869	Dexter, Henry Martyn	Aug. 13, 1821 – Nov. 13, 1890	Boston, Mass.
Oct. 1910	Dexter, Morton	Jul. 12, 1846 – Oct. 29, 1910	Boston, Mass.
Apr. 1925	Dielman, Louis Henry	Jan. 16, 1864 – Mar. 9, 1959	Baltimore, Md.
Oct. 1986	Dietrich, Henry Richard, Jr.	May 12, 1938 –	Chester Springs, Pa.
Dec. 1813	Dinsmore, Silas	Sep., 1776 – Jun. 17, 1847	St. Stephens, Miss.
Apr. 1908	Dionne, Narcisse-Eutrope	May 18, 1848 –	Quebec, Que.
Oct. 1909	Dixon, Roland Burrage	Nov. 6, 1875 – Dec. 19, 1934	Cambridge, Mass.
Jan. 1819	Doane, Guy William	d. Feb. 4, 1862	Circleville, Ohio
Oct. 1961	Dodge, Ernest Stanley	Mar. 18, 1913 – Feb. 9, 1980	Salem, Mass.
Oct. 1862	Dodge, Pickering	Apr. 24, 1804 – Dec. 28, 1863	Philadelphia, Pa.
Apr. 1971	Donald, David Herbert	Oct. 1, 1920 –	Baltimore, Md.
Oct. 1972	Donnelley, Gaylord	May 19, 1910 –	Chicago, Ill.
Apr. 1910	Doughty, Arthur George	d. Dec. 1, 1936	Ottawa, Ont.
Oct. 1910	Dow, George Francis	Jan. 7, 1868 – Jun. 5, 1936	Salem, Mass.
Apr. 1921	Dowse, William Bradford Homer	Feb. 29, 1852 – Apr. 19, 1928	Sherborn, Mass.
Apr. 1878	Doyle, John Thomas	Nov. 26, 1819 – Dec., 1906	San Francisco, Calif.
Oct. 1979	Doyle, Louise		Leominster, Mass.
Apr. 1818	Drake, Daniel	Oct. 20, 1785 – Nov. 6, 1852	Cincinnati, Ohio
Oct. 1877	Draper, Lyman Copeland	Sep. 4, 1815 – Aug. 26, 1891	Madison, Wis.
Oct. 1909	Dresser, Frank Farnham	Oct. 10, 1872 – Sep. 9, 1924	Worcester, Mass.
Oct. 1976	Dumaine, Frederic C., Jr.	Sep. 5, 1902 –	Weston, Mass.
Oct. 1933	Duncan, Winthrop Hillyer	Jun. 24, 1872 – Jul. 20, 1943	Brooklyn, N.Y.
Oct. 1908	Duniway, Clyde Augustus	Nov. 2, 1866 – Dec. 24, 1944	Missoula, Mont.
Apr. 1979	Dunn, Mary Maples	Apr. 6, 1931 –	Bryn Mawr, Pa.
Oct. 1981	Dunn, Richard Slator	Aug. 9, 1928 –	St. Davids, Pa.

Oct. 1912	Dunning, William Archibald	May 12, 1857 – Aug. 25, 1922	New York, N.Y.
Oct. 1816	Du Ponceau, Peter Stephen	Jun. 3, 1760 – Apr. 1, 1844	Philadelphia, Pa.
Apr. 1944	du Pont, Henry Francis	May 27, 1880 – Apr. 10, 1969	Wilmington, Del.
Oct. 1974	Dupree, Anderson Hunter	Jan. 29, 1921 –	Providence, R.I.
Apr. 1976	Duryee, Sacket Roland	Jan. 25, 1909 – Feb. 20, 1985	Worcester, Mass.
Jun. 1821	Dustin, Alexander	Apr. 17, 1776 – Jan. 14, 1837	Westminster, Mass.
Oct. 1855	Duyckinck, Evert Augustus	Nov. 23, 1816 – Aug. 13, 1878	New York, N.Y.
1812	Dwight, Edmund	Nov. 28, 1780 – Apr. 1, 1849	Springfield, Mass.
Apr. 1885	Dwight, Theodore Frelinghuysen	Jun. 11, 1846 – Feb. 3, 1917	Auburn, N.Y.
Sep. 1813	Dwight, Timothy	May 14, 1752 – Jan. 11, 1817	New Haven, Conn.
Apr. 1893	Eames, Wilberforce	Oct. 12, 1855 – Dec. 6, 1937	New York, N.Y.
Apr. 1927	Earle, Ralph	May 3, 1874 – Feb. 13, 1939	Worcester, Mass.
Oct. 1986	Early, Joseph D.	Jan. 31, 1933 –	Worcester, Mass.
Apr. 1884	Early, Samuel Stockwell	Jul., 1857 – Sep. 18, 1884	Terre Haute, Ind.
Apr. 1970	East, Robert Abraham	May 16, 1909 –	New York, N.Y.
Oct. 1814	Ebeling, Christoph Daniel	Nov. 20, 1741 – Jun. 30, 1817	Hamburg, Germany
Apr. 1924	Eddy, George Simpson	Apr. 12, 1867 – Oct. 20, 1947	New York, N.Y.
Aug. 1820	Eddy, Samuel	Mar. 31, 1769 – Feb. 3, 1839	Providence, R.I.
Apr. 1983	Edelman, Hendrik	Nov. 27, 1937 –	New Brunswick, N.J.
Oct. 1978	Edelstein, Jerome Melvin	Jul. 31, 1924 –	Washington, D.C.
Apr. 1885	Edes, Henry Herbert	Mar. 29, 1849 – Oct. 13, 1922	Charlestown, Mass.
Oct. 1918	Edmonds, John Henry	Sep. 29, 1873 – Oct. 27, 1929	Boston, Mass.
Apr. 1893	Eggleston, Edward	Dec. 10, 1837 – Sep. 3, 1902	Lake George, N.Y.
Oct. 1815	Eliot, Samuel	ca. 1772 – Oct. 17, 1821	Washington, D.C.
Oct. 1939	Elkins, William McIntire	Sep. 3, 1882 – Jun. 5, 1947	Philadelphia, Pa.
Oct. 1813	Elliot, Simon	ca. 1762 – Jan. 2, 1832	Newton, Mass.
Oct. 1815	Ellis, Caleb	Apr. 16, 1767 – May 6, 1816	Claremont, N.H.
May 1847	Ellis, George Edward	Aug. 8, 1814 – Dec. 20, 1894	Charlestown, Mass.
Apr. 1947	Ellis, Milton	Aug. 2, 1885 – May 18, 1947	Orono, Maine
May 1843	Elton, Romeo	1790 – Feb. 5, 1870	Providence, R.I.
Apr. 1862	Endicott, William Crowninshield	Nov. 19, 1826 – May 6, 1900	Salem, Mass.
Apr. 1916	Endicott, William Crowninshield	Sep. 28, 1860 – Nov. 28, 1936	Danvers, Mass.
Oct. 1901	Engler, Edmund Arthur	Dec. 23, 1856 – Jan. 16, 1918	Worcester, Mass.
Oct. 1986	Erikson, Dorothy Brewer	Jul. 22, 1920 –	West Boylston, Mass.
Oct. 1816	Erskine, David Steuart	Jun. 1, 1742 – Apr. 19, 1829	Edinburgh, Scotland

Apr. 1961	Erskine, Linwood Mandeville, Jr.	Aug. 28, 1923 –	Paxton, Mass.
Oct. 1834	Erving, George William	Jul. 15, 1769 – Jul. 22, 1850	Paris, France
Aug. 1820	Estabrook, Joseph	Mar. 4, 1759 – Apr. 18, 1830	Athol, Mass.
Oct. 1979	Estes, Joseph Worth	May 10, 1934 –	Westwood, Mass.
Oct. 1930	Esty, Edward Tuckerman	Aug. 30, 1875 – Jul. 4, 1942	Worcester, Mass.
Jul. 1815	Eustis, William	Jun. 10, 1753 – Feb. 6, 1825	Boston, Mass.
Oct. 1910	Evans, Charles	Nov. 13, 1850 – Feb. 8, 1935	Chicago, Ill.
Oct. 1945	Evans, Luther Harris	Oct. 13, 1902 – Dec. 23, 1981	Washington, D.C.
Oct. 1893	*Everett, Charles Carroll	Jun. 19, 1829 – Oct. 16, 1900	Cambridge, Mass.
Jul. 1815	Everett, Edward	Apr. 11, 1794 – Jan. 15, 1865	Boston, Mass.
Oct. 1975	Ewan, Joseph Andorfer	Oct. 24, 1909 –	New Orleans, La.
Oct. 1980	Ewing, Edith Pratt	Oct. 9, 1922 –	Shrewsbury, Mass.
Oct. 1982	Fairbanks, Jonathan Leo	Feb. 19, 1933 –	Boston, Mass.
Oct. 1908	*Farabee, William Curtis	Feb. 7, 1865 – Jun. 24, 1925	Cambridge, Mass.
Apr. 1967	Farber, Daniel	Apr. 14, 1906 –	Worcester, Mass.
Oct. 1942	Farish, Hunter Dickinson	Sep. 12, 1897 – Jan. 16, 1945	Williamsburg, Va.
Oct. 1819	Farmer, John	Jun. 12, 1789 – Aug. 13, 1838	Amherst, N.H.
Oct. 1816	Farnham, John Hay	Jul. 22, 1791 – Jul. 10, 1833	Frankfort, Ky.
Oct. 1946	Farquhar, Francis Peloubet	Dec. 31, 1887 – Nov. 21, 1974	San Francisco, Calif.
Oct. 1876	Farquharson, Robert Jones	d. Sep. 6, 1884	Davenport, Iowa
Oct. 1908	Farrand, Max	Mar. 29, 1869 – Jun. 17, 1945	New Haven, Conn.
Oct. 1975	Farrar, Frederick Breakspear	Jul. 24, 1918 –	New York, N.Y.
Jun. 1814	Farrar, John	Jul. 1, 1779 – May 8, 1853	Cambridge, Mass.
Aug. 1820	Farrelly, Patrick	1770 – Jan. 12, 1826	Meadville, Pa.
Apr. 1915	Farwell, John Whittemore	Apr. 17, 1843 – Oct. 7, 1929	Boston, Mass.
Apr. 1987	Favretti, Rudy John	Dec. 3, 1932 –	Storrs, Conn.
Apr. 1928	Faunce, William Herbert Perry	Jan. 15, 1859 – Jan. 31, 1930	Providence, R.I.
Oct. 1925	Fay, Bernard		Paris, France
Oct. 1816	Fearing, Paul	Feb. 28, 1762 – Aug. 21, 1822	Marietta, Ohio
Oct. 1975	Fehrenbacher, Don Edward	Aug. 21, 1920 –	Stanford, Calif.
May 1842	Felt, Joseph Barlow	Dec. 22, 1789 – Sep. 8, 1869	Boston, Mass.
Oct. 1854	Felton, Cornelius Conway	Nov. 6, 1807 – Feb. 26, 1862	Cambridge, Mass.
Oct. 1980	Fennelly, Catherine Mary	Oct. 24, 1918 –	North Haven, Conn.
Oct. 1976	Fern, Alan Maxwell	Oct. 19, 1930 –	Chevy Chase, Md.
Apr. 1910	Fernald, Merritt Lyndon	Oct. 5, 1873 – Sep. 22, 1950	Cambridge, Mass.
Oct. 1914	Fewkes, Jesse Walter	Nov. 14, 1850 – Mar. 31, 1930	Washington D.C.

* resigned

Oct. 1938	Field, Fred Tarbell	Dec. 24, 1876 – Jul. 23, 1950	Newton, Mass.
Apr. 1981	Fiering, Norman Sanford	Jan. 8, 1935 –	Williamsburg, Va.
Apr. 1978	Filby, Percy William	Dec. 10, 1911 –	Savage, Md.
Oct. 1838	Finlay, George	Dec. 21, 1799 – Jan. 26, 1875	Athens, Greece
Apr. 1928	Finley, John Huston	Oct. 19, 1863 – Mar. 7, 1940	New York, N.Y.
Oct. 1892	Firth, Charles Harding	Mar. 16, 1857 – Feb. 19, 1936	Oxford, England
Apr. 1971	Fischer, David Hackett	Dec. 2, 1935 –	Wayland, Mass.
Oct. 1881	Fischer, Heinrich	Dec. 19, 1817 – Feb. 1, 1886	Freiburg, Germany
Apr. 1911	Fish, Carl Russell	Oct. 17, 1876 – Jul. 10, 1932	Madison, Wis.
Oct. 1879	Fisher, George Park	Aug. 10, 1827 – Dec. 20, 1909	New Haven, Conn.
Oct. 1855	Fisher, Maturin Lewis	Apr. 3, 1807 – Feb. 5, 1879	Farmersville, Iowa
Dec. 1813	Fisk, Moses		White Plains, Tenn.
Apr. 1884	Fiske, John	Mar. 30, 1842 – Jul. 4, 1901	Cambridge, Mass.
Feb. 1813	Fiske, Oliver	Sep. 2, 1762 – Jan. 25, 1837	Worcester, Mass.
Oct. 1815	Fiske, Samuel	Apr. 9, 1769 – Dec. 30, 1834	Claremont, N.H.
Jun. 1813	*Fitch, Ebenezer	Sep. 26, 1756 – Mar. 21, 1833	Williamstown, Mass.
Apr. 1928	Fitzpatrick, John Clement	Aug. 10, 1876 – Feb. 10, 1940	Washington, D.C.
Oct. 1976	Flanagan, Bernard Joseph	Mar. 31, 1908 –	Worcester, Mass.
Apr. 1987	Fleming, Donald Harnish	Aug. 7, 1923 –	Cambridge, Mass.
Apr. 1962	Fletcher, Paris	Jun. 19, 1903 –	Worcester, Mass.
Oct. 1981	Fletcher, Warner Stoddard	Feb. 8, 1945 –	Worcester, Mass.
Oct. 1983	Flynn, Richard Jerome	Jan. 4, 1924 –	Sturbridge, Mass.
Apr. 1950	Flynt, Henry Needham	Jul. 2, 1893 – Aug. 10, 1970	Deerfield, Mass.
Oct. 1849	Folsom, Charles	Dec. 24, 1794 – Nov. 8, 1872	Cambridge, Mass.
Oct. 1831	Folsom, George	May 23, 1802 – Mar. 27, 1869	Worcester, Mass.
Apr. 1887	Foote, Henry Wilder	Jun. 2, 1839 – May 29, 1889	Boston, Mass.
Apr. 1935	Foote, Henry Wilder	Feb. 2, 1875 – Aug. 27, 1964	Belmont, Mass.
Apr. 1921	Forbes, Allan	Nov. 20, 1874 – Jul. 10, 1955	Boston, Mass.
Apr. 1935	Forbes, Allyn Bailey	Nov. 2, 1897 – Jan. 21, 1947	Boston, Mass.
Apr. 1960	Forbes, Esther	Jun. 28, 1891 – Aug. 12, 1967	Worcester, Mass.
Jul. 1825	Forbes, John Murray	Aug. 13, 1771 – Jun. 14, 1831	Buenos Aires, Argentina
Oct. 1986	Forbes, Timothy C.	Oct. 5, 1953 –	New York, N.Y.
Apr. 1896	Forbes, William Trowbridge	May 24, 1850 – Nov. 8, 1931	Westboro, Mass.
Oct. 1851	Force, Peter	Nov. 26, 1790 – Jan. 23, 1868	Washington, D.C.
Apr. 1907	Ford, Worthington Chauncey	Feb. 16, 1858 – Mar. 7, 1941	Washington, D.C.
Oct. 1980	Formisano, Ronald Paul	Mar. 31, 1939 –	Worcester, Mass.
Apr. 1908	Fortier, Alcee	Jun. 5, 1856 – Feb. 14, 1914	New Orleans, La.
Oct. 1831	Foster, Alfred Dwight	Jul. 26, 1800 – Aug. 15, 1852	Worcester, Mass.

* resigned

Oct. 1813	Foster, Dwight	Dec. 7, 1757 – Apr. 29, 1823	Brookfield, Mass.
Oct. 1853	Foster, Dwight	Dec. 13, 1828 – Apr. 18, 1884	Worcester, Mass.
Oct. 1945	Foster, James William	Aug. 10, 1890 – Apr. 30, 1962	Baltimore, Md.
Aug. 1820	Foster, Theodore	Apr. 29, 1752 – Jan. 13, 1828	Foster, R.I.
Oct. 1889	Foster, William Eaton	Jun. 2, 1851 – Sep. 10, 1930	Providence, R.I.
Aug. 1820	Fowle, William Bentley	Oct. 17, 1795 – Feb. 7, 1865	Boston, Mass.
Apr. 1930	Fox, Dixon Ryan	Dec. 7, 1887 – Jan. 30, 1945	Scarsdale, N.Y.
Oct. 1978	*Fox, Francis S.		Lexington, Mass.
Oct. 1906	Fox, George Edward		London, England
Apr. 1886	Francis, George Ebenezer	May 29, 1838 – Nov. 20, 1912	Worcester, Mass.
Oct. 1814	Francis, John Wakefield	Nov. 17, 1789 – Feb. 8, 1861	New York, N.Y.
Apr. 1969	Franklin, John Hope	Jan. 2, 1915 –	Chicago, Ill.
Oct. 1983	Franklin, Ralph William	Aug. 20, 1937 –	New Haven, Conn.
Oct. 1834	Fraser, Charles	Aug. 20, 1782 – Oct. 5, 1860	Charleston, S.C.
Apr. 1983	Frederickson, George Marsh	Jul. 16, 1934 –	Evanston, Ill.
Oct. 1938	Freeman, Douglas Southold	May 16, 1886 – Jun. 13, 1953	Richmond, Va.
Apr. 1885	Freeman, Edward Augustus	Aug. 2, 1823 – May 16, 1892	Oxford, England
Apr. 1984	Freeman, Howard Gilbert	Oct. 31, 1918 –	Worcester, Mass.
Jun. 1814	Freeman, Nathaniel	Mar. 28, 1741 – Sep. 20, 1827	Sandwich, Mass.
Oct. 1814	Freeman, Samuel	Jun. 15, 1743 – Sep. 2, 1831	Portland, Maine
Oct. 1960	Freiberg, Malcolm	Dec. 24, 1919 –	Belmont, Mass.
Apr. 1965	Freidel, Jr., Frank Burt	May 22, 1916 –	Cambridge, Mass.
Oct. 1942	French, Allen	Nov. 28, 1870 – Oct. 6, 1946	Concord, Mass.
Apr. 1852	French, Benjamin Franklin	Jun. 8, 1799 – May 30, 1877	New York, N.Y.
Apr. 1975	French, Hannah Dustin	Aug. 31, 1907 –	Rye, N.H.
Apr. 1938	French, Hollis	Jun. 26, 1868 – Nov. 21, 1940	Boston, Mass.
Oct. 1979	Friary, Donald Richard	Aug. 27, 1940 –	Deerfield, Mass.
Oct. 1979	Fridley, Russell William	Mar. 21, 1928 –	St. Paul, Minn.
Apr. 1952	Friedman, Lee Max	Dec. 29, 1871 – Aug. 7, 1957	Boston, Mass.
Oct. 1814	Fromentin, Eligius	d. Oct. 6, 1822	New Orleans, La.
Apr. 1939	Frost, Donald McKay	May 31, 1877 – Apr. 14, 1958	Boston, Mass.
Oct. 1858	Frothingham, Richard	Jan. 31, 1812 – Jan. 29, 1880	Charlestown, Mass.
Apr. 1933	Fuess, Claude Moore	Jan. 12, 1885 – Sep. 11, 1963	Andover, Mass.
Oct. 1984	Fuld, James Jeffrey	Feb. 16, 1916 –	New York, N.Y.
Apr. 1978	Fuller, Julie Chase	Jul. 30, 1924 –	Holden, Mass.
Jun. 1814	Fulton, Robert	Nov. 14, 1765 – Feb. 24, 1815	New York, N.Y.
Jul. 1825	Funes, Gregorio	d. Jan. 11, 1829	Buenos Aires, Argentina
Oct. 1910	Gage, Homer	Oct. 18, 1861 – Jul. 3, 1938	Worcester, Mass.

* resigned

Apr. 1878	Gage, Thomas Hovey	May 26, 1826 – Sep. 17, 1909	Worcester, Mass.
Oct. 1914	Gage, Thomas Hovey	Jan. 13, 1865 – Jul. 15, 1938	Worcester, Mass.
Jun. 1814	Gahn, Henry		New York, N.Y.
Oct. 1958	Gaines, Pierce Welch	1906 – Jul. 9, 1977	Fairfield, Conn.
May 1836	Galindo, Juan		Central America
May 1836	Gallatin, Albert	Jan. 29, 1761 – Aug. 12, 1849	New York, N.Y.
Apr. 1922	Gamio, Manuel		Mexico City, Mexico
Apr. 1907	Garcia, Genaro	Aug. 17, 1867 – Nov. 26, 1920	Mexico City, Mexico
Oct. 1979	Garrett, Jess Jenkins	Dec. 14, 1914 –	Fort Worth, Tex.
Oct. 1940	Garrett, John Work	May 19, 1872 – Jun. 26, 1942	Baltimore, Md.
Oct. 1968	Garrett, Wendell Douglas	Oct. 9, 1929 –	New York, N.Y.
Oct. 1907	Garrison, George Pierce	Dec. 19, 1853 – Jul. 3, 1910	Austin, Tex.
Oct. 1984	Garvan, Anthony Nicholas Brady	Oct. 4, 1917 –	Philadelphia, Pa.
Oct. 1899	Garver, Austin Samuel	Dec. 12, 1847 – Jun. 20, 1918	Worcester, Mass.
Apr. 1917	Gaskill, George Anthony	Jun. 4, 1877 – Feb. 18, 1940	Worcester, Mass.
Oct. 1814	Gaston, William	Sep. 19, 1778 – Jan. 23, 1844	Raleigh, N.C.
Oct. 1902	Gatschet, Albert Samuel	Oct. 3, 1832 – Mar. 16, 1907	Washington, D.C.
Oct. 1938	Gavit, Joseph	Oct. 10, 1876 – Nov. 28, 1959	Albany, N.Y.
Jun. 1814	Gay, Ebenezer	Feb. 24, 1771 – Feb. 11, 1842	Hingham, Mass.
Apr. 1960	Gay, Ebenezer	Dec. 17, 1925 –	Hingham, Mass.
Oct. 1916	Gay, Ernest Lewis	Dec. 14, 1874 – Nov. 25, 1916	Boston, Mass.
Apr. 1906	Gay, Frederick Lewis	Oct. 28, 1856 – Mar. 3, 1916	Brookline, Mass.
Oct. 1984	Gay, Peter Jack	Jun. 20, 1923 –	Hamden, Conn.
Apr. 1878	Gay, Sydney Howard	May 22, 1814 – Jun. 25, 1888	New York, N.Y.
Oct. 1985	Gemmill, Helen Hartman	Jan. 10, 1918 –	Jamison, Pa.
Apr. 1863	Geoghegan, Thomas G.	d. Dec. 25, 1869	Dublin, Ireland
Oct. 1900	George, Andrew Jackson	Feb. 16, 1855 – Dec. 27, 1907	Brookline, Mass.
Oct. 1983	Gerdts, William Henry	Jan. 18, 1929 –	New York, N.Y.
Oct. 1837	Gerhard, Friedrich Wilhelm Edward	d. May 12, 1867	Berlin, Germany
Apr. 1980	Ghiglione, Loren Frank	Apr. 5, 1941 –	Southbridge, Mass.
Feb. 1813	Gibbs, George	Jan. 7, 1776 – Aug. 5, 1833	Boston, Mass.
Jul. 1826	Gibbs, Josiah Willard	Apr. 30, 1790 – Mar. 25, 1861	New Haven, Conn.
Apr. 1976	Gifford, George Edmund, Jr.	ca. 1931 – Feb. 4, 1981	Watertown, Mass.
Oct. 1815	Gilbert, Benjamin Joseph	Oct. 5, 1764 – Dec. 30, 1849	Hanover, N.H.
Oct. 1900	Gilbert, Edward Hooker	Dec. 7, 1859 – Oct. 7, 1921	Ware, Mass.
Apr. 1931	Gillett, Frederick Huntington	Oct. 16, 1850 – Jul. 31, 1935	Springfield, Mass.

Apr. 1945	Gilman, Bradley Baldwin	Mar. 31, 1904 –	Worcester, Mass.
Oct. 1884	Gilman, Daniel Coit	Jul. 6, 1831 – Oct. 13, 1908	Baltimore, Md.
Jun. 1814	Gilman, John Taylor	Dec. 19, 1753 – Aug. 31, 1828	Portsmouth, N.H.
Apr. 1953	Gimbel, Richard	Jul. 26, 1898 – May 27, 1970	New Haven, Conn.
Apr. 1956	Gipson, Lawrence Henry	Dec. 7, 1880 – Sep. 26, 1971	Rydal, Pa.
Oct. 1887	Gladstone, William Ewart	Dec. 29, 1809 – May 19, 1898	London, England
Oct. 1880	Goddard, Delano Alexander	Aug. 27, 1831 – Jan. 10, 1882	Boston, Mass.
Sep. 1813	Goddard, William	1740 – Dec. 23, 1817	Providence, R.I.
Aug. 1820	Goddard, William Giles	Jan. 2, 1794 – Feb. 16, 1846	Providence, R.I.
Oct. 1974	Goetzmann, William Harry	Jul. 20, 1930 –	Austin, Tex.
Oct. 1949	Goff, Frederick Richmond	Apr. 23, 1916 – Sep. 26, 1982	Washington, D.C.
Oct. 1814	Goldsborough, Charles	Jul. 15, 1765 – Dec. 13, 1834	Annapolis, Md.
Oct. 1814	Goldsborough, Robert Henry	Jan. 4, 1779 – Oct. 5, 1836	New Easton, Md.
Apr. 1987	Goldman, Stephen Alan		Baltimore, Md.
Oct. 1816	Goodhue, Jonathan	Jun. 21, 1783 – Nov. 24, 1848	New York, N.Y.
Aug. 1820	Goodrich, Charles Augustus	Aug. 19, 1790 – Jun. 4, 1862	Worcester, Mass.
Oct. 1921	Goodspeed, Charles Eliot	May 2, 1867 – Oct. 31, 1950	Boston, Mass.
Apr. 1951	Goodspeed, George Talbot	Oct. 10, 1903 –	Boston, Mass.
Jun. 1813	Goodwin, Isaac	Jun. 28, 1786 – Sep. 17, 1832	Sterling, Mass.
Oct. 1893	*Goodwin, William Watson	May 9, 1831 – Jun. 16, 1912	Cambridge, Mass.
Oct. 1844	Gordon, George Hamilton	Jan. 28, 1784 – Dec. 14, 1860	London, England
Jun. 1814	Gore, Christopher	Sep. 21, 1758 – Mar. 1, 1827	Waltham, Mass.
Apr. 1892	Gould, Benjamin Apthorp	Sep. 27, 1824 – Nov. 26, 1896	Cambridge, Mass.
Oct. 1886	Goulding, Frank Palmer	Jul. 2, 1837 – Sep. 16, 1901	Worcester, Mass.
Sep. 1813	Gourgas, John Mark	ca. 1765 – Dec. 8, 1846	Milton, Mass.
Oct. 1940	Graff, Everett Dwight	Aug. 7, 1885 – Mar. 11, 1964	Chicago, Ill.
Apr. 1981	Graham, Donald Edward	Apr. 22, 1945 –	Washington, D.C.
Aug. 1820	Granger, Ebenezer	Jul. 6, 1781 – Sep. 17, 1822	Zanesville, Ohio
Apr. 1910	Grant, William Lawson	d. Feb. 3, 1935	Oxford, England
Aug. 1820	Gray, Francis Calley	Sep. 19, 1790 – Dec. 29, 1856	Boston, Mass.
Oct. 1860	Gray, Horace	Mar. 24, 1828 – Sep. 15, 1902	Boston, Mass.
Aug. 1820	Gray, William	Jun. 27, 1750 – Nov. 3, 1825	Boston, Mass.
Oct. 1889	Green, Andrew Haswell	Oct. 6, 1820 – Nov. 13, 1903	New York, N.Y.
Jun. 1814	Green, Ashbel	Jul. 6, 1762 – May 19, 1848	Princeton, N.J.
Feb. 1813	Green, John	Apr. 19, 1784 – Oct. 17, 1865	Worcester, Mass.
Apr. 1894	Green, John	Apr. 2, 1835 – Dec. 7, 1913	St. Louis, Mo.
Oct. 1865	Green, Samuel Abbott	Mar. 16, 1830 – Dec. 5, 1918	Boston, Mass.
Apr. 1880	Green, Samuel Swett	Feb. 20, 1837 – Dec. 8, 1918	Worcester, Mass.

* resigned

Oct. 1814	Greene, Charles Winston	Jul. 3, 1783 – Dec. 24, 1857	Boston, Mass.
Apr. 1928	Greene, Evarts Boutell	Jul. 8, 1870 – Jun. 24, 1947	New York, N.Y.
Oct. 1972	Greene, Jack Phillip	Aug. 12, 1931 –	Baltimore, Md.
Oct. 1883	Greene, Jeremiah Evarts	Nov. 27, 1834 – Nov. 8, 1902	Worcester, Mass.
Apr. 1983	Greene, John Colton	Mar. 5, 1917 –	Storrs, Conn.
Oct. 1916	Greene, Richard Ward	Dec. 5, 1861 – Mar. 7, 1920	Worcester, Mass.
Aug. 1820	Greenleaf, Moses	Oct. 17, 1777 – Mar. 20, 1834	Portland, Maine
Aug. 1820	Greenleaf, Simon	Dec. 5, 1783 – Oct. 6, 1853	Portland, Maine
Apr. 1891	Greenough, Charles Pelham	Jul. 29, 1844 – Nov. 21, 1924	Brookline, Mass.
Oct. 1927	Greenough, Chester Noyes	Jun. 29, 1874 – Feb. 26, 1938	Cambridge, Mass.
Apr. 1947	Greenslet, Ferris	Jun. 30, 1875 – Nov. 19, 1959	Boston, Mass.
Apr. 1986	Greer, William Hersey, Jr.	Nov. 25, 1928 –	Chevy Chase, Md.
May 1836	Grimke, Frederick	Sep. 1, 1791 – Mar. 8, 1863	Cincinnati, Ohio
Oct. 1833	Grimke, Thomas Smith	Sep. 26, 1786 – Oct. 12, 1834	Charleston, S.C.
Oct. 1981	Grob, Gerald Nat	Apr. 25, 1931 –	Bridgewater, N.J.
Oct. 1982	Gross, Robert Alan	Feb. 17, 1945 –	Falmer, Brighton, England
Apr. 1896	Grosvenor, Edwin Augustus	Aug. 30, 1845 – Sep. 15, 1936	Amherst, Mass.
Apr. 1937	Grosvenor, Gilbert Hovey	Oct. 28, 1875 – Feb. 4, 1976	Washington, D.C.
Apr. 1876	Guild, Reuben Aldridge	May 4, 1822 – May 13, 1899	Providence, R.I.
Jul. 1815	Guilford, Nathan	Jul. 19, 1786 – Dec. 18, 1854	Lexington, Ky.
Apr. 1957	Gummere, Richard Mott	Aug. 3, 1883 – Dec. 3, 1969	Cambridge, Mass.
Apr. 1898	Gunckel, Lewis Winter	Jun. 2, 1869 – Jul. 16, 1916	Dayton, Ohio
Apr. 1982	Gustafson, Otto Vincent	Nov. 2, 1906 –	Worcester, Mass.
Apr. 1977	Guthorn, Peter Jay	Aug. 28, 1916 –	Neptune City, N.J.
Apr. 1983	Haas, Warren James	Mar. 22, 1924 –	Washington, D.C.
Oct. 1977	Haffner, Charles Christian, III	May 27, 1928 –	Chicago, Ill.
Oct. 1927	Hale, Charles Seabury	Jan. 8, 1856 – May 24, 1936	Worcester, Mass.
Oct. 1847	Hale, Edward Everett	Apr. 22, 1822 – Jun. 10, 1909	Worcester, Mass.
Apr. 1961	Hale, Richard Walden, Jr.	Aug. 5, 1909 – Feb. 25, 1976	Chestnut Hill, Mass.
Apr. 1981	Hall, David Drisko	Jul. 8, 1936 –	Arlington, Mass.
Apr. 1875	Hall, Edward Henry	Apr. 16, 1831 – Feb. 22, 1912	Worcester, Mass.
Oct. 1888	Hall, Granville Stanley	Feb. 1, 1846 – Apr. 24, 1924	Worcester, Mass.
Oct. 1894	Hall, Hubert	Jul. 27, 1857 – Jul. 27, 1944	London, England
Apr. 1818	Hall, John Elihu	Dec. 27, 1783 – Jun. 12, 1829	Philadelphia, Pa.
Apr. 1963	Hall, Michael Garibaldi	Jan. 8, 1926 –	Austin, Tex.
Apr. 1977	Hallock, Robert Palmer, Jr.	Oct. 31, 1916 –	Holden, Mass.
Oct. 1813	Halsey, Thomas Lloyd	ca. 1751 – Nov. 12, 1838	Providence, R.I.

Oct. 1813	Halsey, Thomas Lloyd, Jr.	1776 – Feb. 2, 1855	Providence, R.I.
Oct. 1957	Hamilton, Edward Pierce	Feb. 25, 1897 – May 22, 1972	Milton, Mass.
Oct. 1963	Hamilton, Milton Wheaton	Jul. 8, 1901 –	Albany, N.Y.
Apr. 1908	Hamilton, Peter Joseph	Mar. 19, 1859 – Jul. 15, 1927	Mobile, Ala.
Apr. 1947	Hamilton, Sinclair	Oct. 17, 1884 – Aug. 28, 1978	New York, N.Y.
Apr. 1883	Hamlin, Cyrus	Jan. 5, 1811 – Aug. 8, 1900	Middlebury, Vt.
1812	Hammond, Elisha	May 26, 1780 – May 12, 1851	Brookfield, Mass.
Oct. 1957	Hammond, George Peter	Sep. 19, 1896 –	Berkeley, Calif.
Oct. 1914	Hammond, Otis Grant	May 4, 1869 – Oct. 2, 1944	Concord, N.H.
Apr. 1965	Handlin, Oscar	Sep. 29, 1915 –	Cambridge, Mass.
Oct. 1965	Hanna, Archibald, Jr.	Sep. 24, 1916 –	New Haven, Conn.
Jul. 1815	Hanson, Alexander Contee	Feb. 27, 1786 – Apr. 23, 1819	Georgetown, Md.
Oct. 1884	Harden, William	Nov. 11, 1844 – Jan. 4, 1936	Savannah, Ga.
Apr. 1948	Harding, George Laban	1893 – Aug. 30, 1976	Palo Alto, Calif.
Apr. 1972	Hardison, Osborne Bennett	Oct. 22, 1928 –	Washington, D.C.
Oct. 1939	Haring, Clarence Henry	Feb. 9, 1885 – Sep. 4, 1960	Cambridge, Mass.
Apr. 1954	*Harlow, Thompson Ritner		Hartford, Conn.
Oct. 1936	Harper, Lathrop Colgate	1867 – Aug. 11, 1950	New York, N.Y.
Jul. 1815	Harper, Robert Goodloe	Jan., 1765 – Jan. 14, 1825	Baltimore, Md.
Oct. 1960	Harrington, Frank Leighton	Jan. 17, 1902 –	Worcester, Mass.
Apr. 1975	Harrington, Frank Leighton, Jr.	May 26, 1928 –	Weston, Mass.
Oct. 1878	Harris, Clarendon	Sep. 8, 1800 – Jan. 12, 1884	Worcester, Mass.
Oct. 1974	Harris, Elizabeth Massey	Feb. 11, 1940 –	Washington, D.C.
Apr. 1980	Harris, Neil	Jan. 26, 1938 –	Chicago, Ill.
1812	Harris, Thaddeus Mason	Jul. 7, 1768 – Apr. 3, 1842	Dorchester, Mass.
Jun. 1814	Harris, William	Apr. 29, 1765 – Oct. 18, 1829	New York, N.Y.
Oct. 1924	Harrison, Fairfax	Mar. 13, 1869 – Feb. 2, 1938	Belvoir, Va.
Oct. 1969	Harrison, Michael	Dec. 13, 1897 –	Fair Oaks, Calif.
Oct. 1954	Harrison, William Henry	Aug. 1, 1910 – Jul. 3, 1986	Harvard, Mass.
Apr. 1893	Harrisse, Henry	Mar. 24, 1829 – May 13, 1910	Paris, France
Oct. 1909	Hart, Albert Bushnell	Jul. 1, 1854 – Jun. 16, 1943	Cambridge, Mass.
Apr. 1922	Hart, Francis Russell	Jan. 16, 1868 – Jan. 18, 1938	Boston, Mass.
Apr. 1970	Hart, James David	Apr. 18, 1911 –	Berkeley, Calif.
Apr. 1915	Hart, Samuel	Jun. 4, 1845 – Feb. 25, 1917	Middletown, Conn.
Oct. 1964	Harwell, Richard Barksdale	Jun. 6, 1915 –	Brunswick, Maine
Apr. 1968	Haskins, George Lee	Feb. 13, 1915 –	Paoli, Pa.
Oct. 1838	Hassler, Ferdinand Rudolph	Oct. 7, 1770 – Nov. 20, 1843	Washington, D.C.
Apr. 1979	Hatfield, Mark Odom	Jul. 12, 1922 –	Washington, D.C.

* resigned

Jul. 1815	Haven, Nathaniel Appleton	Jan. 14, 1790 – Jun. 3, 1826	Portsmouth, N.H.
Oct. 1838	Haven, Samuel Foster	May 7, 1806 – Sep. 5, 1881	Worcester, Mass.
Dec. 1813	Hawkins, Benjamin	Aug. 15, 1754 – Jun. 6, 1818	Hawkinsville, Ga.
Oct. 1873	Hayden, Ferdinand Vandeveer	Sep. 7, 1829 – Dec. 22, 1887	Washington, D.C.
Apr. 1980	Hayeck, Ernest S.	Jun. 20, 1924 –	Worcester, Mass.
Oct. 1890	Hayes, Rutherford Birchard	Oct. 4, 1822 – Jan. 17, 1893	Fremont, Ohio
Oct. 1896	Haynes, George Henry	Mar. 20, 1866 – Oct. 30, 1947	Worcester, Mass.
Apr. 1881	Haynes, Henry Williamson	Sep. 20, 1831 – Feb. 16, 1912	Boston, Mass.
Dec. 1821	Haywood, John	Mar. 16, 1762 – Dec. 22, 1826	Nashville, Tenn.
Oct. 1973	Hazzard, George William	Oct. 29, 1915 –	Worcester, Mass.
Oct. 1974	Heald, James Nichols, II	Nov. 30, 1927 –	Worcester, Mass.
Apr. 1945	*Heald, Richard Allen	Jul. 2, 1899 – Jun. 17, 1980	Worcester, Mass.
Apr. 1974	Heaney, Howell Johnson	Jul. 7, 1917 –	Philadelphia, Pa.
Oct. 1822	Heckewelder, John Gottlieb Ernestus	Mar. 12, 1743 – Jan. 31, 1823	Bethlehem, Pa.
Oct. 1816	Hedge, Levi	Apr. 19, 1766 – Jan. 3, 1844	Cambridge, Mass.
Oct. 1938	Hedges, James Blaine	Nov. 10, 1891 – Oct. 13, 1965	Providence, R.I.
Apr. 1986	Heimert, Alan Edward	Nov. 10, 1928 –	Cambridge, Mass.
Oct. 1985	Hench, John Bixler	Feb. 21, 1943 –	Worcester, Mass.
Oct. 1924	Henderson, Archibald	Jun. 17, 1877 – Dec. 6, 1963	Chapel Hill, N.C.
Oct. 1977	Henderson, Joseph Welles, Jr.	Aug. 29, 1920 –	Philadelphia, Pa.
Oct. 1985	Henretta, James Aloysius	Nov. 18, 1940 –	College Park, Md.
Oct. 1851	Henry, Joseph	Dec. 17, 1797 – May 13, 1878	Washington, D.C.
Apr. 1893	Henry, William Wirt	Feb. 14, 1831 – Dec. 5, 1900	Richmond, Va.
Oct. 1984	Hequembourg, Frederick Williams	Apr. 25, 1917 –	Ballston Lake, N.Y.
Jul. 1815	Herron, Francis	Jun. 28, 1774 – Dec. 6, 1860	Pittsburgh, Pa.
Apr. 1961	Heslin, James Joseph	Jun. 25, 1916 –	New York, N.Y.
Aug. 1820	Heywood, Benjamin Franklin	Apr. 24, 1792 – Dec. 7, 1869	Worcester, Mass.
Apr. 1965	Hiatt, Jacob	Jul. 1, 1909 –	Worcester, Mass.
Oct. 1926	Higgins, Aldus Chapin	Dec. 7, 1872 – Sep. 10, 1948	Worcester, Mass.
Apr. 1934	Higgins, John Woodman	Sep. 1, 1874 – Aug. 19, 1961	Worcester, Mass.
Oct. 1948	Higgins, Milton Prince	Oct. 29, 1903 –	Worcester, Mass.
Oct. 1970	Higgins, Richard Carney	Nov. 23, 1937 –	Worcester, Mass.
Oct. 1874	*Higginson, Thomas Wentworth	Dec. 22, 1823 – May 9, 1911	Newport, R.I.

* resigned

Oct. 1976	Higham, John	Oct. 26, 1920 –	Baltimore, Md.
Apr. 1818	Hildreth, Samuel Prescott	Sep. 30, 1783 – Jul. 24, 1863	Marietta, Ohio
Oct. 1831	Hill, Alonzo	Jun. 20, 1800 – Feb. 1, 1871	Worcester, Mass.
Apr. 1901	Hill, Benjamin Thomas	Mar. 22, 1863 – Nov. 9, 1927	Worcester, Mass.
Apr. 1908	Hill, Don Gleason	Jul. 12, 1847 – Feb. 20, 1914	Dedham, Mass.
Apr. 1890	Hill, Hamilton Andrews	Apr. 14, 1827 – Apr. 27, 1895	Boston, Mass.
Oct. 1816	Hill, Mark Langdon	Jun. 30, 1772 – Nov. 26, 1842	Phippsburg, Maine
Dec. 1813	Hillhouse, James	Oct. 20, 1754 – Dec. 29, 1832	New Haven, Conn.
Apr. 1972	Hindle, Brooke	Sep. 28, 1918 –	Ridgewood, N.J.
Apr. 1876	*Hitchcock, Edward	May 23, 1828 – Feb. 15, 1911	Amherst, Mass.
Jun. 1814	Hitchcock, Gad	Nov. 2, 1749 – Nov. 29, 1836	Scituate, Mass.
Apr. 1882	Hitchcock, Henry	Jul. 3, 1829 – Mar. 18, 1902	St. Louis, Mo.
Oct. 1962	Hitchings, Sinclair Hamilton	Sep. 19, 1933 –	Boston, Mass.
Apr. 1969	Hitchman, Robert Bruce	Oct. 28, 1908 – Apr. 17, 1981	Seattle, Wash.
Oct. 1891	Hoadley, Charles Jeremy	Aug. 1, 1828 – Oct. 19, 1900	Hartford, Conn.
Oct. 1963	Hoagland, Hudson	Dec. 5, 1899 – Mar. 4, 1982	Southboro, Mass.
Oct. 1853	Hoar, George Frisbie	Aug. 29, 1826 – Sep. 30, 1904	Worcester, Mass.
Apr. 1894	Hoar, Rockwood	Aug. 24, 1855 – Nov. 1, 1906	Worcester, Mass.
Oct. 1814	Hobart, John Henry	Sep. 14, 1775 – Sep. 12, 1830	New York, N.Y.
Oct. 1908	Hodge, Frederick Webb	Oct. 28, 1864 – Sep. 28, 1956	Washington, D.C.
Oct. 1910	Hoffman, Samuel Verplanck	May 12, 1866 – Feb. 23, 1942	New York, N.Y.
Apr. 1970	Hofstadter, Richard	Aug. 6, 1916 – Oct. 24, 1970	New York, N.Y.
Oct. 1948	Holbrook, Stewart Hall	Aug. 22, 1893 – Sep. 3, 1964	Portland, Oreg.
Oct. 1928	Holdsworth, William Searle	May 7, 1871 – Jan. 2, 1944	Oxford, England
Oct. 1816	Holley, Horace	Feb. 13, 1781 – Jul. 31, 1827	Boston, Mass.
Apr. 1935	Hollingsworth, Valentine	Jul. 11, 1883 – Dec. 10, 1942	Boston, Mass.
Apr. 1915	Hollis, Ira Nelson	Mar. 7, 1856 – Aug. 15, 1930	Worcester, Mass.
Feb. 1813	Holmes, Abiel	Dec. 24, 1763 – Jun. 4, 1837	Cambridge, Mass.
Apr. 1963	Holmes, Oliver Wendell	Feb. 2, 1902 – Nov. 25, 1981	Washington, D.C.
Apr. 1927	Holmes, Thomas James	Dec. 26, 1874 – Feb. 7, 1959	Cleveland, Ohio
Oct. 1905	Holmes, William Henry	Dec. 1, 1846 – Apr. 20, 1933	Washington, D.C.
Oct. 1882	Holst, Hermann Eduard von	Jun. 19, 1841 – Jan. 20, 1904	Freiburg, Germany
Apr. 1987	Hood, Graham		Williamsburg, Va.
Aug. 1820	Hooker, John	Oct. 8, 1761 – Mar. 7, 1829	Springfield, Mass.
Oct. 1958	Hoopes, Penrose Robinson	Mar. 17, 1892 – Jan. 14, 1976	Philadelphia, Pa.
Apr. 1983	Horgan, Paul	Aug. 1, 1903 –	Middletown, Conn.
Apr. 1938	Hornblower, Henry	Jun. 8, 1863 – Apr. 11, 1941	Boston, Mass.
Oct. 1975	Hornblower, Henry, II	Nov. 5, 1917 – Oct. 20, 1985	Chestnut Hill, Mass.

* resigned

Oct. 1814	Hosack, David	Aug. 31, 1769 – Dec. 22, 1835	New York, N.Y.
Apr. 1985	Hosmer, Herbert Henry		S. Lancaster, Mass.
Apr. 1918	Hosmer, James Kendall	Jan. 29, 1834 – May 11, 1927	Minneapolis, Minn.
Apr. 1968	Houghton, Arthur Amory, Jr.	Dec. 12, 1906 –	New York, N.Y.
Apr. 1857	Houghton, George Frederick	May 31, 1820 – Sep. 22, 1870	St. Albans, Vt.
Oct. 1984	Housh, Emmett William	Feb. 15, 1932 –	Sherborn, Mass.
Jul. 1815	Howard, John Eager	Jun. 4, 1752 – Oct. 12, 1827	Baltimore, Md.
Apr. 1932	Howay, Frederic William	Nov. 25, 1867 – Oct. 4, 1943	New Westminster, B.C.
Oct. 1925	Howe, Mark Antony DeWolfe	Aug. 24, 1864 – Dec. 6, 1960	Boston, Mass.
Apr. 1954	*Howe, Parkman Dexter	Sep. 20, 1889 – Jan. 13, 1980	Needham, Mass.
Apr. 1875	Hoyt, Albert Harrison	Dec. 6, 1826 – Jun. 10, 1915	Boston, Mass.
Apr. 1894	Hubbard, Gardiner Greene	Aug. 25, 1822 – Dec. 11, 1897	Washington, D.C.
Apr. 1853	Hubbard, Samuel Dickinson	Aug. 10, 1799 – Oct. 8, 1855	Middletown, Conn.
Oct. 1881	Hübbe, Joaquin	Jan. 1, 1832 – Dec. 31, 1901	Merida, Yucatan
May 1844	Hudson, Charles	Nov. 14, 1795 – May 4, 1881	Westminster, Mass.
Apr. 1894	Hudson, John Elbridge	Aug. 3, 1839 – Oct. 1, 1900	Boston, Mass.
Oct. 1980	Huggins, Nathan Irvin	Jan. 14, 1927 –	Cambridge, Mass.
Apr. 1960	Hugo, Harold	Aug. 8, 1910 – Sep. 9, 1985	Meriden, Conn.
Apr. 1861	Huguet-Latour, Louis Adolphe	ca. 1830 – May, 1904	Montreal, Que.
Apr. 1912	Hulbert, Archer Butler	Jan. 26, 1873 – Dec. 24, 1933	Marietta, Ohio
Apr. 1908	Hull, Charles Henry	Sep. 29, 1864 – Jul. 15, 1936	Ithaca, N.Y.
Oct. 1816	Humboldt, Alexander von	Sep. 14, 1769 – May 6, 1859	Paris, France
Dec. 1821	Humboldt, Karl Wilhelm von	Jun. 22, 1767 – Apr. 8, 1835	Berlin, Germany
Oct. 1951	Hume, Edgar Erskine	Dec. 26, 1889 – Jan. 24, 1952	Washington, D.C.
Oct. 1971	Humelsine, Carlisle Hubbard	Mar. 12, 1915 –	Williamsburg, Va.
Dec. 1813	Humphreys, David	Jul. 10, 1752 – Feb. 21, 1818	Boston, Mass.
Oct. 1869	Hunnewell, James Frothingham	Jul. 3, 1832 – Nov. 11, 1910	Charlestown, Mass.
Apr. 1927	Hunnewell, James Melville	May 22, 1879 – Mar. 22, 1954	Boston, Mass.
Jun. 1813	Hunt, David	ca. 1773 – Jul. 8, 1837	Northampton, Mass.
Apr. 1910	Hunt, Gaillard	Sep. 8, 1862 – Mar. 20, 1924	Washington, D.C.
Oct. 1819	Hunt, William Gibbes	Feb. 21, 1791 – Aug. 13, 1833	Lexington, Ky.
Oct. 1947	Hunter, Dard	Nov. 29, 1883 – Feb. 20, 1966	Chillicothe, Ohio

* resigned

Oct. 1856	Hunter, Joseph	Feb. 6, 1783 – May 9, 1861	London, England
Jul. 1815	Hunter, William	Nov. 26, 1774 – Dec. 3, 1849	Newport, R.I.
Apr. 1910	Huntington, Archer Milton	Mar. 10, 1870 – Dec. 11, 1955	New York, N.Y.
Apr. 1915	Huntington, Henry Edwards	Feb. 27, 1850 – May 23, 1927	New York, N.Y.
Oct. 1875	Huntington, William Reed	Sep. 20, 1838 – Jul. 26, 1909	Worcester, Mass.
Oct. 1950	Hutchinson, Elmer Tindall	Sep. 10, 1882 – Sep. 13, 1954	Elizabeth, N.J.
Oct. 1952	Hyde, James Hazen	Jun. 6, 1876 – Jul. 26, 1959	New York, N.Y.
Apr. 1881	Icazbalceta, Joaquin Garcia	Aug. 21, 1825 – Nov. 26, 1894	Mexico City, Mexico
Jul. 1815	Inglis, James	1777 – Aug. 15, 1820	Baltimore, Md.
Oct. 1981	Ireland, Genevieve Rogers Weeks		Shrewsbury, Mass.
Jul. 1815	Irving, Washington	Apr. 3, 1783 – Nov. 28, 1859	Philadelphia, Pa.
Oct. 1933	Isham, Norman Morrison	Nov. 12, 1864 – Jan. 1, 1943	Providence, R.I.
Apr. 1966	Jackman, Sydney Wayne	Mar. 25, 1925 –	Victoria, B.C.
Apr. 1818	Jackson, Andrew	Mar. 15, 1767 – Jun. 8, 1845	Nashville, Tenn.
Oct. 1976	Jackson, Donald Dean	Jun. 10, 1919 –	Charlottesville, Va.
Apr. 1968	Jackson, Frederick Herbert	May 16, 1919 –	Worcester, Mass.
Apr. 1855	Jackson, Henry	Jun. 16, 1798 – Mar. 2, 1863	Newport, R.I.
Oct. 1882	Jackson, James	Sep. 9, 1843 – Jul. 17, 1895	Paris, France
Oct. 1819	Jackson, John		Cincinnati, Ohio
Jul. 1815	Jackson, Richard	Jul. 3, 1764 – Apr. 18, 1838	Providence, R.I.
Oct. 1943	Jackson, William Alexander	Jul. 25, 1905 – Oct. 4, 1964	Cambridge, Mass.
Oct. 1976	Jacobson, M Howard	Mar. 27, 1933 –	Worcester, Mass.
1812	James, Eleazer	ca. 1754 – Apr. 4, 1843	Barre, Mass.
Apr. 1919	James, James Alton	Sep. 17, 1864 – Feb. 12, 1962	Evanston, Ill.
Oct. 1890	Jameson, John Franklin	Sep. 19, 1859 – Sep. 28, 1937	Providence, R.I.
Oct. 1816	Jamieson, John	Mar., 1759 – Jul. 12, 1838	Edinburgh, Scotland
Apr. 1943	Jantz, Harold Stein	Aug. 26, 1907 – Feb. 27, 1987	Princeton, N.J.
Apr. 1854	Jarvis, Edward	Jan. 9, 1803 – Oct. 31, 1884	Dorchester, Mass.
Jan. 1815	Jarvis, Samuel Farmar	Jan. 20, 1786 – Mar. 26, 1851	New York, N.Y.
Jun. 1814	Jay, John	Dec. 12, 1745 – May 17, 1829	New York, N.Y.
Jun. 1814	Jay, Peter Augustus	Jan. 24, 1776 – Feb. 20, 1843	New York, N.Y.
Apr. 1953	Jefferson, Howard Bonar	Sep. 28, 1901 – Oct. 1, 1983	Worcester, Mass.
Jun. 1814	Jefferson, Thomas	Apr. 13, 1743 – Jul. 4, 1826	Monticello, Va.
Jan. 1819	Jenckes, William Scott		Havana, Cuba
Apr. 1915	Jenkins, Lawrence Waters	Dec. 23, 1872 – Apr. 20, 1961	Salem, Mass.
Apr. 1901	Jenks, Henry Fitch	Oct. 17, 1842 – Jan. 31, 1920	Canton, Mass.
Feb. 1813	Jenks, William	Nov. 25, 1778 – Nov. 13, 1866	Bath, Maine
Oct. 1914	Jenney, Charles Francis	Sep. 16, 1860 – Nov. 29, 1923	Hyde Park, Mass.

Apr. 1964	Jennings, John Melville	Oct. 22, 1916 –	Richmond, Va.
Jun. 1814	Jennison, Samuel	Feb. 24, 1788 – Mar. 11, 1860	Worcester, Mass.
Oct. 1884	Jennison, Samuel	Jan. 30, 1821 – Sep. 21, 1900	Boston, Mass.
Oct. 1969	Jensen, Merrill Monroe	Jul. 16, 1905 – Jan. 30, 1980	Madison, Wis.
Oct. 1974	Jensen, Oliver Ormerod	Apr. 16, 1914 –	Old Saybrook, Conn.
Oct. 1961	Jeppson, John, II	Dec. 10, 1916 –	Worcester, Mass.
Oct. 1851	Jewett, Charles Coffin	Aug. 12, 1816 – Jan. 9, 1868	Washington, D.C.
Oct. 1955	Johnson, Alden Porter	Mar. 24, 1914 – Sep. 8, 1972	Worcester, Mass.
Oct. 1922	Johnson, Alfred	Jun. 28, 1871 – Jan. 13, 1933	Brookline, Mass.
Oct. 1925	Johnson, Allen	Jan. 29, 1870 – Jan. 18, 1931	New Haven, Conn.
Oct. 1978	Johnson, Edward Crosby, III	Jun. 29, 1930 –	Boston, Mass.
Oct. 1893	*Johnson, Edward Francis	Oct. 22, 1856 –	Woburn, Mass.
Apr. 1982	Johnson, Minna Flynn	May 7, 1915 –	Worcester, Mass.
Oct. 1893	Johnston, Henry Phelps	Apr. 19, 1842 – Feb. 28, 1923	New York, N.Y.
Jul. 1815	Johnston, Robert	d. May 20, 1861	Meadville, Pa.
Oct. 1893	Johnston, William Preston	Jan. 5, 1831 – Jul. 16, 1899	New Orleans, La.
Oct. 1855	Jomard, Edme Francois	d. Sep. 25, 1862	Paris, France
Apr. 1869	Jones, Charles Colcock	Oct. 28, 1831 – Jul. 19, 1893	New York, N.Y.
Oct. 1972	Jones, Gordon Willis	Aug. 20, 1915 –	Fredericksburg, Va.
Oct. 1867	Jones, Horatio Gates	Jan. 9, 1822 – Mar. 14, 1893	Philadelphia, Pa.
Apr. 1956	Jones, Howard Mumford	Apr. 16, 1892 – May 11, 1980	Cambridge, Mass.
Jun. 1814	Jones, John Coffin	Jun. 8, 1750 – Oct. 25, 1829	Boston, Mass.
Oct. 1877	Jones, Joseph	Sep. 6, 1833 – Feb. 17, 1896	New Orleans, La.
Oct. 1978	Jones, Kenneth Schwalm	May 12, 1906 –	Shrewsbury, Mass.
Oct. 1924	Jones, Matt Bushnell	May 15, 1871 – Jul. 1, 1940	Boston, Mass.
Sep. 1813	Jones, William	Oct. 8, 1753 – Apr. 9, 1822	Providence, R.I.
Oct. 1915	Jordan, John Woolf	Sep. 14, 1840 – Jun. 11, 1921	Philadelphia, Pa.
Apr. 1970	Jordan, Winthrop Donaldson	Nov. 11, 1931 –	Berkeley, Calif.
Oct. 1977	Josephy, Alvin M., Jr.	May 18, 1915 –	Greenwich, Conn.
Apr. 1986	Joyce, William Leonard	Mar. 29, 1942 –	Princeton, N.J.
May 1847	Judd, Sylvester	Apr. 23, 1789 – Apr. 17, 1860	Northampton, Mass.
Oct. 1917	Jusserand, Jean Jules	Feb. 18, 1855 – Jul. 18, 1932	Paris, France
Apr. 1975	Kammen, Michael Gedaliah	Oct. 25, 1936 –	Ithaca, N.Y.
Apr. 1855	Kane, Elisha Kent	Feb. 3, 1820 – Feb. 16, 1857	Philadelphia, Pa.
Apr. 1927	Kane, Grenville	Jul. 12, 1854 – Jul. 17, 1943	New York, N.Y.
Oct. 1983	Kaplan, Jeremiah	Jul. 15, 1926 –	New York, N.Y.
Apr. 1986	Kaplan, Sidney	Mar. 1, 1913 –	Amherst, Mass.
Oct. 1966	Kaser, David	Mar. 12, 1924 –	Nashville, Tenn.
Apr. 1981	Katz, Stanley Nider	Apr. 23, 1934 –	Princeton, N.J.

* resigned

Apr. 1987	Keating, William John	Mar. 30, 1927 –	Detroit, Mich.
Apr. 1918	Kelby, Robert Hendre	Aug. 31, 1847 – Aug. 25, 1927	New York, N.Y.
Oct. 1908	Kellen, William Vail	Jul. 3, 1852 – Dec. 20, 1942	Boston, Mass.
Apr. 1875	Keller, Otto		Freiburg, Germany
Apr. 1961	Kemble, John Haskell	Jun. 17, 1912 –	Claremont, Calif.
Oct. 1951	Kendall, Henry Plympton	Jan. 15, 1878 – Nov. 3, 1959	Boston, Mass.
Oct. 1984	Kennedy, Roger George	Aug. 3, 1926 –	Washington, D.C.
Oct. 1929	Kent, Henry Watson	Sep. 28, 1866 – Aug. 28, 1948	New York, N.Y.
Jun. 1814	Kent, James	Jul. 31, 1763 – Dec. 13, 1847	Chancellor, N.Y.
Oct. 1965	Kenyon, Cecelia Marie	Nov. 28, 1922 –	Northampton, Mass.
Oct. 1924	Keogh, Andrew	Nov. 14, 1869 – Feb. 13, 1953	New Haven, Conn.
Oct. 1981	Kerber, Linda Kaufman	Jan. 23, 1940 –	Iowa City, Iowa
Oct. 1984	Ketcham, Ralph Louis	Oct. 28, 1927 –	Syracuse, N.Y.
Apr. 1983	Ketchum, Richard Malcolm	Mar. 15, 1922 –	Dorset, Vt.
Apr. 1916	Kidder, Nathaniel Thayer	Oct. 29, 1860 – Jul. 13, 1938	Milton, Mass.
Apr. 1937	Kimball, Leroy Elwood	Oct. 31, 1888 – Nov. 27, 1962	New York, N.Y.
Apr. 1970	King, Bruce Anthony	Feb. 23, 1934 –	Southboro, Mass.
Apr. 1865	King, Jonas	Jul. 29, 1792 – May 22, 1869	Athens, Greece
Oct. 1980	King, Patricia Miller	Jul. 26, 1937 –	Cambridge, Mass.
Jun. 1814	King, Rufus	Mar. 24, 1755 – Apr. 29, 1827	New York, N.Y.
Apr. 1886	Kingsbury, Frederick John	Jan. 1, 1823 – Sep. 30, 1910	Waterbury, Conn.
Apr. 1930	Kingsley, Darwin Pearl	May 5, 1857 – Oct. 6, 1932	New York, N.Y.
Apr. 1896	Kinnicutt, Leonard Parker	May 22, 1854 – Feb. 6, 1911	Worcester, Mass.
Oct. 1906	Kinnicutt, Lincoln Newton	Mar. 14, 1849 – Dec. 13, 1921	Worcester, Mass.
Oct. 1953	Kinnicutt, Roger	Feb. 12, 1880 – Feb. 2, 1961	Worcester, Mass.
May 1842	Kinnicutt, Thomas	Nov. 30, 1800 – Jan. 22, 1858	Worcester, Mass.
Oct. 1978	Kirkendall, Richard Stewart	Apr. 11, 1928 –	Bloomington, Ind.
Oct. 1948	Kirkland, Edward Chase	May 24, 1894 – May 24, 1975	Brunswick, Maine
1812	Kirkland, John Thornton	Aug. 17, 1770 – Apr. 26, 1840	Boston, Mass.
Oct. 1901	Kittredge, George Lyman	Feb. 28, 1860 – Jul. 23, 1941	Cambridge, Mass.
Apr. 1924	Kittredge, Henry Crocker	Jan. 4, 1890 – Feb. 12, 1967	Concord, N.H.
Oct. 1986	Klein, Milton Martin	Aug. 15, 1917 –	Knoxville, Tenn.
Oct. 1975	Klyberg, Albert T.	Aug. 8, 1940 –	Providence, R.I.
Jun. 1814	Knapp, Samuel Lorenzo	Jan. 19, 1783 – Jul. 8, 1838	Newburyport, Mass.
Oct. 1909	Knapp, Shepherd	Sep. 8, 1873 – Jan. 11, 1946	Worcester, Mass.
Oct. 1931	Knauss, James Owen	1885 – Aug. 29, 1970	Kalamazoo, Mich.
Apr. 1964	Knight, Russell Wallace	Feb. 4, 1903 –	Marblehead, Mass.
Oct. 1940	Knollenberg, Bernhard	Nov. 26, 1892 – Jul. 6, 1973	New Haven, Conn.
Oct. 1976	Knowlton, Elliott Burris	Sep. 30, 1914 –	Holden, Mass.

Oct. 1945	Knox, Dudley Wright	Jun. 21, 1877 – Jun. 11, 1960	Washington, D.C.
Apr. 1984	Kohlstedt, Sally Gregory	Jan. 30, 1943 –	Cortland, N.Y.
Oct. 1969	Kohn, John Sicher van Eisen	Oct. 6, 1906 – Dec. 18, 1976	White Plains, N.Y.
Oct. 1965	Korn, Bertram Wallace	Oct. 6, 1918 – Dec. 11, 1979	Philadelphia, Pa.
Oct. 1908	Kroeber, Alfred Louis	Jun. 11, 1876 – Oct. 5, 1960	San Francisco, Calif.
Apr. 1979	Kugler, Richard Cory	Jun. 8, 1930 –	New Bedford, Mass.
Oct. 1985	Kupperman, Karen Ordahl	Apr. 23, 1939 –	Storrs, Conn.
Oct. 1970	*Kurtz, Stephen Guild	Sep. 9, 1926 –	Williamsburg, Va.
Oct. 1965	Labaree, Benjamin Woods	Jul. 21, 1927 –	Williamstown, Mass.
Apr. 1943	Labaree, Leonard Woods	Aug. 26, 1897 – May 5, 1980	New Haven, Conn.
Jul. 1825	Lafayette, Gilbert Motier De	Sep. 6, 1757 – May 20, 1834	La Grange, France
Apr. 1972	Lamar, Howard Roberts	Nov. 18, 1923 –	New Haven, Conn.
Oct. 1964	Lamb, William Kaye	May 11, 1904 –	Ottawa, Ont.
Oct. 1883	Lamson, Charles Marion	May 16, 1843 – Aug. 8, 1899	Worcester, Mass.
Apr. 1946	Lancour, Harold	Jun. 27, 1908 – Oct. 23, 1981	New York, N.Y.
Apr. 1982	Land, Aubrey Christian	Sep. 2, 1912 –	Athens, Ga.
Apr. 1974	Lane, Mills Bee, IV	Aug. 22, 1942 –	Savannah, Ga.
Oct. 1978	Lane, Saundra Baker	Sep. 3, 1938 –	Lunenburg, Mass.
Apr. 1908	Lane, William Coolidge	Jul. 29, 1859 – Mar. 18, 1931	Cambridge, Mass.
Oct. 1973	Langdon, John Emerson	Apr. 13, 1902 – Sep. 27, 1981	Toronto, Ont.
Oct. 1888	Langley, Samuel Pierpont	Aug. 22, 1934 – Feb. 27, 1906	Washington, D.C.
Apr. 1978	Lank, David Morris	Nov. 25, 1937 –	Montreal, Que.
Apr. 1853	Lapham, Increase Allen	Mar. 7, 1811 – Sep. 14, 1875	Milwaukee, Wis.
Oct. 1981	Lapides, Julian Lee	Sep. 17, 1931 –	Baltimore, Md.
Apr. 1911	Latane, John Holladay	Apr. 1, 1869 – Jan. 1, 1932	Lexington, Va.
Apr. 1961	Lathem, Edward Connery	Dec. 15, 1926 –	Hanover, N.H.
Dec. 1813	Lathrop, John	May 6, 1740 – Jan. 4, 1816	Boston, Mass.
Sep. 1813	Lathrop, John, Jr.	Jan. 13, 1772 – Jan. 30, 1820	Boston, Mass.
Jul. 1815	Latrobe, Benjamin Henry	May 1, 1764 – Sep. 3, 1820	Pittsburgh, Pa.
Oct. 1925	Lawler, Thomas Bonaventure	Jul. 14, 1864 – Jul. 20, 1945	New York, N.Y.
Oct. 1846	Lawrence, Abbott	Dec. 16, 1792 – Aug. 18, 1855	Boston, Mass.
Apr. 1857	Lawrence, Timothy Bigelow	Nov. 22, 1826 – Mar. 21, 1869	Boston, Mass.
Oct. 1899	Lawrence, William	May 30, 1850 – Nov. 6, 1941	Boston, Mass.
Oct. 1862	Lawton, William	May 1, 1795 – Apr. 27, 1881	New Rochelle, N.Y.
Oct. 1888	Lea, Henry Charles	Sep. 19, 1825 – Oct. 24, 1909	Philadelphia, Pa.
Jun. 1814	Lear, Tobias	Sep. 19, 1762 – Oct. 11, 1816	Washington, D.C.
Apr. 1975	Leary, Lewis	Apr. 18, 1906 –	Chapel Hill, N.C.

* resigned

Apr. 1891	Lecky, William Edward Hartpole	Mar. 26, 1838 – Oct. 23, 1903	London, England
Oct. 1904	Lee, Francis Henry	Dec. 23, 1836 – Oct. 8, 1913	Salem, Mass.
Apr. 1917	Lee, John Thomas	Nov. 6, 1875 – Apr. 26, 1953	Madison, Wis.
Apr. 1940	Lefavour, Henry	Sep. 4, 1862 – Jun. 16, 1946	Boston, Mass.
Apr. 1919	Lehmann, Frederick William	Feb. 28, 1853 – Sep. 12, 1931	St. Louis, Mo.
Oct. 1924	Leland, Waldo Gifford	Jul. 17, 1879 – Oct. 17, 1966	Washington, D.C.
Oct. 1971	Lemay, Joseph Alberic Leo	Jan. 17, 1935 –	Los Angeles, Calif.
Apr. 1854	Lenox, James	Aug. 19, 1800 – Feb. 17, 1880	New York, N.Y.
Oct. 1890	Leon, Nicolas	ca. 1857 – Jan. 23, 1929	Morelia, Mexico
Apr. 1878	*Le Plongeon, Augustus	1826 – Dec. 13, 1908	New York, N.Y.
Oct. 1976	Lerner, Gerda	Apr. 30, 1920 –	Astoria, N.Y.
Apr. 1983	Le Roy, Bruce Murdock	Jun. 9, 1920 –	Tacoma, Wash.
Oct. 1814	Lescallier, Daniel	Nov. 4, 1743 – May, 1822	New York, N.Y.
Apr. 1905	Levasseur, Pierre Emile	d. Jul. 10, 1911	Paris, France
Apr. 1978	Levin, David	Nov. 21, 1924 –	Charlottesville, Va.
Apr. 1970	Levy, Leonard Williams	Apr. 9, 1923 –	LaVerne, Calif.
Oct. 1816	Lewis, Isaac	Jan. 1, 1773 – Sep. 23, 1854	New Rochelle, N.Y.
Oct. 1944	Lilly, Josiah Kirby, Jr.	Sep. 25, 1893 – May 4, 1966	Indianapolis, Ind.
Oct. 1974	Lilly, Josiah Kirby, III	ca. 1917 –	West Falmouth, Mass.
Apr. 1919	Lima, Manuel De Oliveira	Dec. 25, 1867 – Mar. 24, 1928	Rio De Janeiro, Brazil
Apr. 1984	Lincoln, Crawford	Aug. 18, 1928 –	Sturbridge, Mass.
Apr. 1869	Lincoln, Daniel Waldo	Jan. 16, 1813 – Jul. 1, 1880	Worcester, Mass.
Oct. 1924	Lincoln, Daniel Waldo	Sep. 2, 1882 – Mar. 16, 1971	Worcester, Mass.
Jan. 1819	Lincoln, Enoch	Dec. 28, 1788 – Oct. 8, 1829	Fryeburg, Maine
Oct. 1840	Lincoln, John Waldo	Jun. 14, 1787 – Oct. 2, 1852	Worcester, Mass.
1812	Lincoln, Levi	May 15, 1749 – Apr. 14, 1820	Worcester, Mass.
1812	Lincoln, Levi, Jr.	Oct. 25, 1782 – May 29, 1868	Worcester, Mass.
Apr. 1920	Lincoln, Merrick	May 25, 1875 – Sep. 2, 1923	Worcester, Mass.
Oct. 1861	Lincoln, Solomon	Dec. 28, 1804 – Dec. 1, 1881	Hingham, Mass.
Apr. 1882	Lincoln, Solomon	Aug. 14, 1838 – Oct. 15, 1907	Boston, Mass.
Apr. 1898	Lincoln, Waldo	Dec. 31, 1849 – Apr. 7, 1933	Worcester, Mass.
Jul. 1825	Lincoln, William	Sep. 26, 1802 – Oct. 5, 1843	Worcester, Mass.
Apr. 1948	Little, Bertram Kimball	Jul. 27, 1899 –	Brookline, Mass.
Oct. 1855	Little, Charles Coffin	Jul. 25, 1799 – Aug. 9, 1869	Cambridge, Mass.
Apr. 1967	Little, David Britton	Nov. 1, 1912 –	Concord, Mass.
Oct. 1967	Little, Nina Fletcher	Jan. 25, 1903 –	Brookline, Mass.

* resigned

Apr. 1912	Littlefield, George Emery	Aug. 29, 1844 – Sep. 4, 1915	Boston, Mass.
Apr. 1984	Litwack, Leon Frank	Dec. 2, 1929 –	Berkeley, Calif.
Oct. 1815	Livermore, Edward St. Loe	Apr. 5, 1762 – Sep. 15, 1832	Boston, Mass.
Oct. 1849	Livermore, George	Jul. 9, 1809 – Aug. 31, 1865	Cambridge, Mass.
Oct. 1897	Livermore, William Roscoe	Jan. 11, 1843 – Sep. 28, 1919	Boston, Mass.
Oct. 1833	Livingston, Edward	May 28, 1764 – May 23, 1836	New York, N.Y.
Jun. 1814	Livingston, Henry Brockholst	Nov. 26, 1757 – Mar. 19, 1823	New York, N.Y.
Jul. 1815	Livingston, Jasper Hall	d. Aug. 9, 1835	Jamaica, West Indies
Oct. 1914	Livingston, Luther Samuel	Jul. 7, 1864 – Dec. 24, 1914	Cambridge, Mass.
Aug. 1820	Lloyd, James	Dec., 1769 – Apr. 5, 1831	Boston, Mass.
Oct. 1927	Lockwood, Luke Vincent	Feb. 1, 1872 – Jan. 23, 1951	New York, N.Y.
Oct. 1881	Lodge, Henry Cabot	May 12, 1850 – Nov. 9, 1924	Nahant, Mass.
Oct. 1913	Lombard, Herbert Edwin	Nov. 19, 1863 – Jul. 13, 1940	Worcester, Mass.
Oct. 1896	Lord, Arthur	Sep. 2, 1850 – Apr. 10, 1925	Plymouth, Mass.
Dec. 1813	Lord, Nathaniel, III	Sep. 25, 1780 – Oct. 16, 1852	Ipswich, Mass.
Oct. 1936	Loring, Augustus Peabody	Apr. 16, 1885 – Oct. 1, 1951	Boston, Mass.
Oct. 1955	Loring, Augustus Peabody, III	Aug. 24, 1915 – Nov. 27, 1986	Salem, Mass.
Apr. 1862	Loring, Charles Greely	May 2, 1794 – Oct. 8, 1867	Boston, Mass.
Oct. 1872	Lossing, Benson John	Feb. 12, 1813 – Jun. 3, 1891	New York, N.Y.
Apr. 1897	Loubat, Joseph Florimond	Jan. 21, 1831 – Mar. 1, 1927	Paris, France
Apr. 1894	Love, William DeLoss	Nov. 29, 1851 – Apr. 8, 1918	Hartford, Conn.
Apr. 1975	Lowance, Mason Ira, Jr.	Jun. 2, 1938 –	Amherst, Mass.
Apr. 1899	Lowell, Abbott Lawrence	Dec. 13, 1856 – Jan. 6, 1943	Boston, Mass.
Oct. 1814	Lowell, Charles	Aug. 15, 1782 – Jan. 20, 1861	Boston, Mass.
Apr. 1895	Lowell, Francis Cabot	Jan. 7, 1855 – Mar. 6, 1911	Boston, Mass.
Oct. 1959	Lowens, Irving	Aug. 19, 1916 – Nov. 14, 1983	Hyattsville, Md.
May 1844	Lower, Mark Anthony	Jul. 14, 1813 – Mar. 22, 1876	Lewes, England
Oct. 1963	Lownes, Albert Edgar	May 10, 1899 – Nov. 17, 1978	Providence, R.I.
Oct. 1893	Lubbock, John	Apr. 30, 1834 – May 28, 1913	Farnborough, England
Oct. 1984	Lundquist, Weyman Ivan	Jul. 27, 1930 –	San Francisco, Calif
Apr. 1933	Lydenberg, Harry Miller	Nov. 18, 1874 – Apr. 4, 1960	New York, N.Y.
Jul. 1815	Lyman, Daniel	Jan. 27, 1756 – Oct. 16, 1830	Providence, R.I.
1812	Lyman, Jonathan Hunt	Jun. 13, 1783 – Nov. 3, 1825	Northampton, Mass.
Sep. 1813	Lyman, Joseph	Apr. 14, 1749 – Mar. 27, 1828	Hatfield, Mass.
Apr. 1902	Lyman, William Denison	Dec. 1, 1852 – Jun. 21, 1920	Walla Walla, Wash.

Oct. 1978	Lynes, Joseph Russell	Dec. 2, 1910 –	New York, N.Y.
Oct. 1915	McAdie, Alexander George	Aug. 4, 1863 – Nov. 1, 1943	Milton, Mass.
Dec. 1813	McCall, Hugh	1767 – Jun. 10, 1824	Savannah, Ga.
Oct. 1901	McCall, Samuel Walker	Feb. 28, 1851 – Nov. 4, 1923	Winchester, Mass.
May 1846	McCaul, John	1807 – Apr. 16, 1897	Toronto, Ont.
Sep. 1813	Maccarty, Nathaniel	Jul. 10, 1758 – Oct. 14, 1831	Worcester, Mass.
Oct. 1982	McClelland, Jr., John Morris	May 31, 1915 –	Bellevue, Wash.
Apr. 1855	McClure, Robert John Le Mesurier	Jan. 28, 1807 – Oct. 17, 1873	London, England
Apr. 1960	McCorison, Marcus Allen	Jul. 17, 1926 –	Iowa City, Iowa
Oct. 1928	McCoy, James Comly	1862 – 1934	Grasse, France
Jun. 1813	McCulloh, James Hugh		Baltimore, Md.
Apr. 1961	McDermott, John Francis	Apr. 18, 1902 – Apr. 23, 1981	St. Louis, Mo.
Apr. 1948	McDonald, Gerald Doan	Jun. 5, 1905 – May 6, 1970	New York, N.Y.
Oct. 1982	McDonald, John Peter	Oct. 17, 1922 –	Storrs, Conn.
Oct. 1902	MacDonald, William	Jul. 31, 1863 – Dec. 15, 1938	Providence, R.I.
Jul. 1815	McDowell, John	Sep. 10, 1780 – Feb. 16, 1863	Elizabeth, N.J.
Oct. 1983	McFeely, William Shield	Sep. 25, 1930 –	South Hadley, Mass.
Oct. 1935	McGregor, Tracy William	Apr. 14, 1869 – May 6, 1936	Washington, D.C.
Oct. 1906	Machado, Bernardino	d. Apr. 29, 1944	Coimbra, Portugal
Jul. 1815	McHenry, James	Nov. 16, 1753 – May 3, 1816	Baltimore, Md.
Oct. 1918	MacKall, Leonard Leopold	Jan. 29, 1879 – May 19, 1937	Savannah, Ga.
Apr. 1944	McKay, George Leslie	Oct. 12, 1895 – Jan. 17, 1976	New York, N.Y.
Jul. 1815	Mackenzie, Roderick		Montreal, Que.
Jun. 1814	McKesson, John	d. Jun., 1829	New York, N.Y.
Oct. 1974	McKibbin, David Milton Kendall	Oct. 15, 1906 – Mar. 28, 1978	Boston, Mass.
Apr. 1818	McKinney, John Augustine	d. May 12, 1845	Rogersville, Tenn.
Apr. 1908	McLaughlin, Andrew Cunningham	Feb. 14, 1861 – Sep. 24, 1947	Chicago, Ill.
Oct. 1973	McLoughlin, William Gerald, Jr.	Jun. 11, 1922 –	Providence, R.I.
May 1836	Maclure, William	Oct. 27, 1763 – Mar. 23, 1840	Philadelphia, Pa.
Apr. 1884	McMaster, John Bach	Jun. 29, 1852 – May 24, 1932	Philadelphia, Pa.

Oct. 1974	MacNeil, Neil	Jan. 3, 1923 –	Silver Spring, Md.
Oct. 1977	McNeil, Robert Lincoln, Jr.	Jul. 13, 1915 –	Wyndmoor, Pa.
Apr. 1973	McNiff, Philip James	Feb. 10, 1912 –	Chestnut Hill, Mass.
Apr. 1818	Madison, James	Mar. 16, 1751 – Jun. 28, 1836	Montpelier, Va.
May 1836	Magnusen, Finn	d. Dec. 24, 1847	Copenhagen, Denmark
Apr. 1977	Maguire, James Robert	Jul. 5, 1924 –	Shoreham, Vt.
Oct. 1976	Maier, Pauline Rubbelke	Apr. 27, 1938 –	Boston, Mass.
Apr. 1987	Main, Gloria Lund	Jun. 1, 1933 –	Boulder, Colo.
Oct. 1972	Main, Jackson Turner	Aug. 6, 1917 –	Setauket, N.Y.
Apr. 1977	Majno, Guido	Feb. 9, 1922 –	Shrewsbury, Mass.
Apr. 1974	Mallary, Gertrude Robinson	Aug. 19, 1902 –	Bradford, Vt.
Apr. 1934	Malone, Dumas	Jan. 10, 1892 – Dec. 27, 1986	Washington, D.C.
Oct. 1984	Manoog, Russell Elliott	Jul. 23, 1934 –	Worcester, Mass.
Oct. 1881	March, Francis Andrew	Oct. 25, 1825 – Sep. 9, 1911	Easton, Pa.
Oct. 1851	Marsh, George Perkins	Mar. 15, 1801 – Jul. 23, 1882	Constantinople, Turkey
Oct. 1893	Marsh, Henry Alexander	Sep. 7, 1836 – Nov. 6, 1914	Worcester, Mass.
Oct. 1877	Marsh, Othniel Charles	Oct. 29, 1831 – Mar. 18, 1899	New Haven, Conn.
Oct. 1860	Marsh, Sidney Harper	Aug. 29, 1825 – Feb. 2, 1879	Forest Grove, Oreg.
Oct. 1816	Marshall, Alexander Keith	1770 – Feb. 7, 1825	Washington, Ky.
Dec. 1813	Marshall, John	Sep. 24, 1755 – Jul. 6, 1835	Washington, D.C.
Oct. 1833	Martin, Francois Xavier	Mar. 17, 1762 – Dec. 10, 1846	New Orleans, La.
Apr. 1968	Martin, Henry Bradley	Mar. 27, 1906 –	New York, N.Y.
Apr. 1978	Marty, Martin Emil	Feb. 5, 1928 –	Riverside, Ill.
Oct. 1974	Martz, Louis Lohr	Sep. 27, 1913 –	New Haven, Conn.
Apr. 1985	Marx, Leo	Nov. 15, 1919 –	Boston, Mass.
Oct. 1974	Mason, Charles Ellis, Jr.	Oct. 5, 1908 –	Chestnut Hill, Mass.
Oct. 1887	Mason, Edward Gay	Aug. 23, 1839 – Dec. 18, 1898	Chicago, Ill.
Oct. 1941	Mason, Henry Lowell	Aug. 14, 1864 – Oct. 18, 1957	Boston, Mass.
Jul. 1815	Mason, Jeremiah	Apr. 27, 1768 – Oct. 14, 1848	Portsmouth, N.H.
Apr. 1869	Mason, John Edwin	Sep. 28, 1831 – Mar. 5, 1892	Washington, D.C.
Jun. 1814	Mason, John Mitchell	Mar. 19, 1770 – Dec. 26, 1829	New York, N.Y.
Oct. 1908	Mason, Otis Tufton	Apr. 10, 1838 – Nov. 5, 1908	Washington, D.C.
Oct. 1922	Mason, William Smith	Dec. 8, 1866 – Jan. 11, 1961	Evanston, Ill.
Oct. 1977	Massey, Robert Keiser	May 25, 1914 –	Holden, Mass.

Oct. 1920	Mather, William Gwinn	Sep. 22, 1857 – Apr. 5, 1951	Cleveland, Ohio
Oct. 1855	Mather, William Williams	May 24, 1804 – Feb. 26, 1859	Columbus, Ohio
Oct. 1974	Matheson, John William	Jun. 14, 1927 –	Washington, D.C.
Oct. 1982	Mathews, Forrest David	Dec. 6, 1935 –	Dayton, Ohio
Oct. 1901	Matthews, Albert	Jun. 26, 1860 – Apr. 13, 1946	Boston, Mass.
Oct. 1910	Maudslay, Alfred Percival	1850 – Jan. 22, 1931	London, England
Oct. 1877	Maxwell, Thomas	Jan. 30, 1815 – ca. 1877	Tuscaloosa, Ala.
Oct. 1978	May, Henry Farnham	Mar. 27, 1915 –	Berkeley, Calif.
Apr. 1857	Mayer, Brantz	Sep. 27, 1809 – Feb. 23, 1879	Baltimore, Md.
Oct. 1928	Mayo, Lawrence Shaw	Jun. 26, 1888 – Jul. 23, 1947	West Newton, Mass.
Apr. 1891	Mead, Edwin Doak	Sep. 29, 1849 – Aug. 17, 1937	Boston, Mass.
Oct. 1976	Meagher, John Henry	Dec. 7, 1908 –	Worcester, Mass.
Apr. 1935	Means, Philip Ainsworth	Apr. 3, 1892 – Nov. 24, 1944	Pomfret, Conn.
Oct. 1966	Mearns, David Chambers	Dec. 31, 1899 – May 21, 1981	Washington, D.C.
Jul. 1825	Mease, James	Aug. 11, 1771 – May 14, 1846	Philadelphia, Pa.
Apr. 1909	Medina, Jose Toribio	Oct. 21, 1852 – Dec. 11, 1930	Santiago, Chile
Apr. 1935	Melcher, Frederick Gershom	Apr. 12, 1879 – Mar. 9, 1963	New York, N.Y.
Apr. 1861	Mellen, Edward	Sep. 26, 1802 – May 24, 1875	Worcester, Mass.
Apr. 1967	Mellon, Paul	Jun. 11, 1907 –	Upperville, Va.
Oct. 1980	Melville, Donald Robert	Nov. 18, 1926 –	Worcester, Mass.
Oct. 1917	Membreno, Alberto	Jul. 12, 1859 – Feb. 4, 1921	Tegucigalpa, Honduras
Apr. 1895	Mendenhall, Thomas Corwin	Oct. 4, 1841 – Mar. 22, 1924	Worcester, Mass.
Apr. 1881	Mendoza, Gumesindo	1829 – Feb. 6, 1886	Mexico City, Mexico
Apr. 1946	Merk, Frederick	Aug. 15, 1887 – Sep. 24, 1977	Belmont, Mass.
Oct. 1888	Merriam, John McKinstry	Sep. 20, 1862 – Jan. 9, 1959	Framingham, Mass.
Jul. 1826	Merrick, Pliny	Aug. 2, 1794 – Jan. 31, 1867	Worcester, Mass.
Oct. 1815	Merrill, James Cushing	Sep. 27, 1784 – Oct. 4, 1853	Boston, Mass.
Apr. 1884	Merriman, Daniel	Dec. 3, 1838 – Sep. 18, 1912	Worcester, Mass.
Oct. 1902	Merriman, Roger Bigelow	May 24, 1876 – Sep. 7, 1945	Cambridge, Mass.
Apr. 1928	Merritt, Edward Percival	Mar. 28, 1860 – Apr. 16, 1932	Boston, Mass.
Jul. 1815	Messer, Asa	Mar. 31, 1769 – Oct. 11, 1836	Providence, R.I.
Oct. 1937	Metcalf, Frank Johnson	Apr. 4, 1865 – Feb. 25, 1945	Washington, D.C.
Apr. 1867	Metcalf, John George	Sep. 10, 1801 – Jan. 12, 1892	Mendon, Mass.
Oct. 1937	Metcalf, Keyes De Witt	Apr. 13, 1889 – Nov. 3, 1983	Cambridge, Mass.
May 1844	Metcalf, Theron	Oct. 16, 1784 – Nov. 13, 1875	Boston, Mass.
Apr. 1958	Middendorf, John William	Sep. 22, 1924 –	Greenwich, Conn.

Oct. 1983	Middlekauff, Robert Lawrence	Jul. 5, 1929 –	San Marino, Calif.
Apr. 1976	Miller, Amy Bess Williams		Pittsfield, Mass.
Oct. 1973	Miller, Clarence William	Jun. 5, 1914 –	Landsdowne, Pa.
Apr. 1978	Miller, Harold Taylor	Jan. 5, 1923 –	Lincoln, Mass.
Jun. 1821	Miller, James	Apr. 25, 1776 – Jul. 7, 1851	Post of Ark, Ark. Terr.
Apr. 1976	Miller, Lawrence Kelton		Pittsfield, Mass.
Apr. 1975	*Miller, Paul	Sep. 28, 1906 –	Rochester, N.Y.
Apr. 1938	Miller, Perry Gilbert Eddy	Feb. 25, 1905 – Dec. 9, 1963	Cambridge, Mass.
Sep. 1813	Miller, Samuel	Oct. 31, 1769 – Jan. 7, 1850	New York, N.Y.
Apr. 1930	Miller, William Davis	Nov. 5, 1887 – Jul. 7, 1959	Providence, R.I.
1812	Mills, Elijah Hunt	Dec. 1, 1776 – May 5, 1829	Northampton, Mass.
Apr. 1870	Milnes, Richard Monckton	Jun. 19, 1809 – Aug. 11, 1885	London, England
Apr. 1925	Minot, Joseph Grafton	Jan. 13, 1858 – Jun. 19, 1939	Boston, Mass.
Apr. 1981	Mirick, John Odlen	Nov. 27, 1946 –	Worcester, Mass.
Oct. 1931	Mitchell, Robert Stewart	Nov. 25, 1892 – Nov. 1, 1957	Boston, Mass.
Jun. 1814	Mitchill, Samuel Latham	Aug. 20, 1764 – Sep. 7, 1831	New York, N.Y.
May 1845	Mittermaier, Karl Joseph Anton	d. Aug. 29, 1867	Heidelberg, Germany
Oct. 1870	Mommsen, Christian Matthias Theodor	Nov. 30, 1817 – Nov. 1, 1903	Berlin, Germany
Apr. 1818	Monroe, James	Apr. 28, 1758 – Jul. 4, 1831	Washington, D.C.
Oct. 1958	Montgomery, Charles Franklin	Apr. 14, 1910 – Feb. 21, 1978	Winterthur, Del.
May 1836	Montmorency, A.C.F., Duke of	Jul. 12, 1767 – May 26, 1846	Paris, France
Apr. 1953	Moody, Robert Earle	Mar. 30, 1901 – Apr. 7, 1983	Boston, Mass.
Oct. 1967	Mooney, James Eugene	May 13, 1932 –	Worcester, Mass.
Apr. 1895	Moore, Clarence Bloomfield	Jan. 14, 1852 – Mar. 24, 1936	Philadelphia, Pa.
Oct. 1921	Moore, George Foot	Oct. 15, 1851 – May 16, 1931	Cambridge, Mass.
Apr. 1880	Moore, George Henry	Apr. 20, 1823 – May 5, 1892	New York, N.Y.
Dec. 1821	Moore, Jacob Bailey	Oct. 31, 1797 – Sep. 1, 1853	Concord, N.H.
Jul. 1815	Moore, Jesse	d. Nov. 22, 1824	Meadville, Pa.
Aug. 1820	Moore, Robert	Mar. 30, 1778 – Jan. 14, 1831	Beaver, Pa.
Oct. 1834	Moreau, Cesar	d. Nov. 26, 1861	Paris, France

* resigned

Jul. 1825	Moreno, Manuel	1781 – Dec. 18, 1857	Buenos Aires, Argentina
Apr. 1983	Morgan, Anne Murray	Aug. 2, 1925 –	Worcester, Mass.
Apr. 1949	Morgan, Edmund Sears	Jan. 17, 1916 –	Providence, R.I.
Apr. 1924	Morgan, John Hill	Jun. 30, 1870 – Jul. 16, 1945	Brooklyn, N.Y.
Oct. 1865	Morgan, Lewis Henry	Nov. 21, 1818 – Dec. 17, 1881	Rochester, N.Y.
Oct. 1926	Morgan, Paul Beagary	May 7, 1869 – Nov. 3, 1952	Worcester, Mass.
Oct. 1972	Morgan, Peter Shepard	Nov. 24, 1924 –	Leicester, Mass.
Apr. 1966	Morgan, Weld	Nov. 14, 1908 – Nov. 8, 1983	Worcester, Mass.
Apr. 1982	Morison, Elting Elmore	Dec. 14, 1909 –	Peterborough, N.H.
Apr. 1914	Morison, Samuel Eliot	Jul. 9, 1887 – May 15, 1976	Boston, Mass.
Jun. 1814	Morris, Gouverneur	Jan. 31, 1752 – Nov. 6, 1816	New York, N.Y.
Oct. 1854	Morris, Oliver Bliss	Sep. 22, 1782 – Apr. 11, 1871	Springfield, Mass.
Apr. 1969	Morris, Richard Brandon	Jul. 24, 1904 –	Mt. Vernon, N.Y.
Oct. 1814	Morrow, Jeremiah	Oct. 6, 1771 – Mar. 22, 1852	Ohio Territory
Apr. 1903	Morse, Anson Daniel	Aug. 13, 1846 – Mar. 13, 1916	Amherst, Mass.
Apr. 1898	Morse, Edward Sylvester	Jun. 13, 1838 – Dec. 20, 1925	Salem, Mass.
Apr. 1932	Morse, Glenn Tilley	Jul. 30, 1870 – Jun. 22, 1950	West Newbury, Mass.
Feb. 1813	Morse, Jedediah	Aug. 23, 1761 – Jun. 9, 1826	Charlestown, Mass.
Oct. 1815	Morse, Samuel Finley Breese	Apr. 27, 1791 – Apr. 2, 1872	Charlestown, Mass.
May 1844	Morton, Samuel George	Jan. 26, 1799 – May 15, 1851	Philadelphia, Pa.
Oct. 1925	Moses, Horace Augustus	Apr. 21, 1862 – Apr. 22, 1947	Springfield, Mass.
Oct. 1856	Motley, John Lothrop	Apr. 15, 1814 – May 29, 1877	Boston, Mass.
Oct. 1941	Mott, Frank Luther	Apr. 4, 1886 – Oct. 23, 1964	Iowa City, Iowa
Oct. 1986	Moynihan, Daniel Patrick	Mar. 16, 1927 –	Washington, D.C.
Oct. 1985	Moynihan, Kenneth James	Jul. 27, 1944 –	Worcester, Mass.
Oct. 1893	Mozoomdar, Protap Chunder	Oct., 1840 – May 27, 1905	Calcutta, India
Jun. 1814	Muhlenberg, Henry Augustus	May 13, 1782 – Aug. 11, 1844	Philadelphia, Pa.
Oct. 1970	Mumey, Nolie	Feb. 8, 1891 – Jan. 22, 1984	Denver, Colo.
Apr. 1909	Munro, Wilfred Harold	Aug. 20, 1849 – Aug. 9, 1934	Providence, R.I.
Apr. 1854	Munsell, Joel	Apr. 14, 1808 – Jan. 15, 1880	Albany, N.Y.
Apr. 1818	Munson, Jeremiah Raleigh		Greenville, Ohio
Oct. 1918	Munson, Samuel Lyman	Jun. 6, 1844 – May 19, 1930	Albany, N.Y.
Oct. 1857	Murchison, Roderic Impey	Feb. 19, 1792 – Oct. 22, 1871	London, England

Apr. 1922	Murdock, Harold	Jan. 16, 1862 – Apr. 5, 1934	Brookline, Mass.
Apr. 1924	Murdock, Kenneth Ballard	Jun. 22, 1895 – Nov. 15, 1975	Boston, Mass.
Apr. 1987	Murphy, Franklin David	Jan. 29, 1916 –	Beverly Hills, Calif.
Oct. 1981	Murrill, Paul Whitefield	Jul. 10, 1934 –	Baton Rouge, La.
Oct. 1964	Nadeau, Gabriel	Mar. 20, 1900 – Jan. 31, 1979	Rutland, Mass.
Apr. 1941	Nash, Chauncey Cushing	Oct. 17, 1884 – Jul. 16, 1968	Boston, Mass.
Oct. 1985	Nash, Gary Baring	Jul. 27, 1933 –	Pacific Palisades, Calif.
Apr. 1955	Nash, Ray	Feb. 27, 1905 – May 21, 1982	Hanover, N.H.
Oct. 1813	Nash, William	Aug. 5, 1768 – Mar. 25, 1829	West Boylston, Mass.
Oct. 1865	Nason, Elias	Apr. 21, 1811 – Jun. 17, 1887	Exeter, N.H.
Oct. 1814	Nason, Reuben	Apr. 7, 1779 – Jan. 15, 1835	Freeport, Maine
Apr. 1973	Nebenzahl, Kenneth	Sep. 16, 1927 –	Glencoe, Ill.
Apr. 1984	Neilly, Andrew Hutchinson, Jr.	Dec. 23, 1923 –	New York, N.Y.
Oct. 1878	Nelson, Thomas Leverett	Mar. 4, 1827 – Nov. 21, 1897	Worcester, Mass.
Apr. 1909	Nelson, William	Feb. 10, 1847 – Aug. 10, 1914	Paterson, N.J.
Apr. 1941	Nevins, Allan	May 20, 1890 – Mar. 5, 1971	New York, N.Y.
Oct. 1860	Newberry, John Strong	Dec. 22, 1822 – Dec. 7, 1892	Cleveland, Ohio
Apr. 1977	Newman, Eric Pfeiffer	May 25, 1911 –	St. Louis, Mo.
Jul. 1815	Newton, Rejoice	Oct. 18, 1782 – Apr. 2, 1868	Worcester, Mass.
Oct. 1816	Nichols, Benjamin Ropes	May 18, 1786 – Apr. 30, 1848	Salem, Mass.
Apr. 1897	Nichols, Charles Lemuel	May 29, 1851 – Feb. 19, 1929	Worcester, Mass.
Oct. 1978	Nichols, Frederick Doveton	Jul. 1, 1911 –	Charlottesville, Va.
Oct. 1971	Nichols, James Hastings	Jan. 18, 1915 –	Princeton, N.J.
May 1838	Nicolas, Nicholas Harris	Mar. 10, 1799 – Aug. 3, 1848	London, England
Oct. 1982	Nissenbaum, Stephen Willner	Jan. 13, 1941 –	Amherst, Mass.
Apr. 1856	Noailles, Paul De	d. May 30, 1885	Paris, France
Jul. 1815	Noble, Habijah Weld	d. May 10, 1816	Marietta, Ohio
Oct. 1898	Noble, John	Apr. 14, 1829 – Jun. 10, 1909	Boston, Mass.
Oct. 1816	Noble, Mark	1754 – May 26, 1827	Barming, England
Oct. 1945	Noe, Sydney Philip	Apr. 4, 1885 – Jun. 4, 1969	New York, N.Y.
Oct. 1986	Noël Hume, Ivor	Sep. 30, 1927 –	Williamsburg, Va.
Apr. 1914	Norcross, Grenville Howland	Feb. 2, 1854 – Feb. 12, 1937	Boston, Mass.
Apr. 1976	Norton, Mary Beth	Mar. 25, 1943 –	Ithaca, N.Y.
Jun. 1814	Nott, Eliphalet	Jun. 25, 1773 – Jan. 29, 1866	Schenectady, N.Y.
Oct. 1883	Nourse, Henry Stedman	Apr. 9, 1831 – Nov. 14, 1903	Lancaster, Mass.

Oct. 1980	Novak, Barbara Jane		New York, N.Y.
Apr. 1984	Nunis, Doyce Blackman, Jr.	May 30, 1924 –	Los Angeles, Calif.
Apr. 1971	Nye, Russel Blaine	Feb. 17, 1913 –	East Lansing, Mich.
Oct. 1984	Nylander, Jane Cayford	Jan. 27, 1938 –	Sturbridge, Mass.
Oct. 1893	Ober, Frederick Albion	Feb. 13, 1849 – Jun. 1, 1913	Washington, D.C.
Oct. 1922	Obregon, Luis Gonzalez	ca. 1866 – Jun. 19, 1938	Mexico City, Mexico
Oct. 1900	O'Brien, Michael Charles	Oct. 20, 1842 – Nov. 11, 1901	Bangor, Maine
Oct. 1928	O'Brien, Robert Lincoln	Sep. 14, 1865 – Nov. 23, 1955	Boston, Mass.
Oct. 1927	Ochs, Adolph Simon	Mar. 12, 1858 – Apr. 8, 1935	New York, N.Y.
Apr. 1987	O'Connor, Thomas D.		Loudonville, N.Y.
Apr. 1945	Odell, George Clinton Densmore	Mar. 19, 1866 – Oct. 17, 1949	New York, N.Y.
Apr. 1904	*O'Dowd, John	d. Nov. 19, 1919	Portland, Maine
Apr. 1891	Olcott, George	Jul. 11, 1838 – Apr. 10, 1895	Charlestown, N.H.
Apr. 1953	Olds, Irving Sands	Jan. 22, 1887 – Mar. 4, 1963	New York, N.Y.
Apr. 1961	Oliver, Andrew	Mar. 14, 1906 – Oct. 20, 1981	New York, N.Y.
Oct. 1913	Oliver, Vere Langford	d. Jan. 9, 1942	Sunninghill, England
Apr. 1908	Osgood, Herbert Levi	Apr. 9, 1855 – Sep. 11, 1918	New York, N.Y.
Apr. 1960	Osgood, William Bradford	Mar. 15, 1928 –	Boston, Mass.
Oct. 1822	Otis, George Alexander	d. Jun. 18, 1831	Quincy, Mass.
1812	Otis, Harrison Gray	Oct. 8, 1765 – Oct. 28, 1848	Boston, Mass.
Apr. 1983	Otto, Calvin Peter	Apr. 19, 1930 –	Bennington, Vt.
Aug. 1820	Overton, John	Apr. 9, 1766 – Apr. 12, 1833	Nashville, Tenn.
Oct. 1907	Owen, Thomas Mc Adory	Dec. 15, 1866 – Mar. 25, 1920	Montgomery, Ala.
Oct. 1878	Paige, Lucius Robinson	Mar. 8, 1802 – Sep. 2, 1896	Cambridge, Mass.
Jan. 1815	Paine, Amasa	d. Dec. 25, 1823	Troy, N.Y.
Dec. 1813	Paine, Elijah	Jan. 21, 1757 – Apr. 28, 1842	Williamstown, Vt.
Jun. 1813	Paine, Frederick William	May 23, 1788 – Sep. 16, 1869	Worcester, Mass.
Apr. 1867	Paine, George Sturgis	Jun. 4, 1833 – Aug. 2, 1908	Worcester, Mass.
1812	Paine, Nathaniel	Jan. 5, 1759 – Oct. 7, 1840	Worcester, Mass.
Oct. 1860	Paine, Nathaniel	Aug. 6, 1832 – Jan. 14, 1917	Worcester, Mass.
Oct. 1926	Paine, Russell Sturgis	Jun. 6, 1871 – Jan. 3, 1959	Worcester, Mass.
Nov. 1812	Paine, William	Jun. 5, 1750 – Apr. 17, 1833	Worcester, Mass.
Apr. 1856	Palfrey, John Gorham	May 2, 1796 – Apr. 26, 1881	Cambridge, Mass.
Apr. 1860	Palgrave, Francis	1788 – Jul. 6, 1861	Hampstead, England
Oct. 1983	Palm, Marion Stedman	Mar. 10, 1928 –	Leicester, Mass.
Oct. 1914	Palmer, William Pendleton	Jun. 17, 1861 – Dec. 17, 1927	Cleveland, Ohio

* resigned

Apr. 1904	Paltsits, Victor Hugo	Jul. 12, 1867 – Oct. 3, 1952	New York, N.Y.
Oct. 1969	Papantonio, Michael	Feb. 25, 1907 – Aug. 20, 1978	New York, N.Y.
Apr. 1987	Papenfuse, Edward Carl, Jr.	Oct. 15, 1943 –	Annapolis, Md.
Apr. 1987	Pappas, Arthur Michael	Jul. 3, 1931 –	Weston, Mass.
Oct. 1947	Pargellis, Stanley	Jun. 25, 1898 – Jan. 6, 1968	Chicago, Ill.
Dec. 1813	Parish, Elijah	Nov. 7, 1762 – Oct. 15, 1825	Byfield, Mass.
Apr. 1917	Park, Charles Edwards	Mar. 14, 1873 – Sep. 23, 1962	Boston, Mass.
Oct. 1831	Park, John	Jan. 7, 1775 – Mar. 2, 1852	Worcester, Mass.
Oct. 1916	Park, Lawrence	Dec. 16, 1873 – Sep. 28, 1924	Groton, Mass.
Dec. 1821	Park, Thomas	1759 – Nov. 26, 1834	Hampstead, England
Oct. 1910	Parker, Henry Ainsworth	Oct. 19, 1841 – Feb. 17, 1919	Cambridge, Mass.
Oct. 1819	Parker, Isaac	Jun. 17, 1768 – Jul. 25, 1830	Boston, Mass.
Apr. 1977	Parker, John	May 15, 1923 –	Minneapolis, Minn.
Apr. 1818	Parkman, Francis	Jun. 4, 1788 – Nov. 12, 1852	Boston, Mass.
Oct. 1865	Parkman, Francis	Sep. 16, 1823 – Nov. 8, 1893	Boston, Mass.
Apr. 1932	Parsons, Edward Alexander	Mar. 28, 1878 – Feb. 19, 1962	New Orleans, La.
Oct. 1813	Parsons, Theophilus	Feb. 24, 1750 – Oct. 30, 1813	Boston, Mass.
May 1843	Parsons, Usher	Aug. 18, 1788 – Dec. 19, 1868	Providence, R.I.
Jun. 1814	Partridge, George	Feb. 8, 1740 – Jul. 7, 1828	Duxbury, Mass.
Jul. 1815	Patterson, Robert	May 30, 1743 – Jul. 22, 1824	Pittsburgh, Pa.
Apr. 1924	Patterson, William Davis	Mar. 5, 1858 – Jul. 16, 1931	Wiscasset, Maine
Apr. 1980	Paul, Rodman Wilson	Nov. 6, 1912 – May 15, 1987	Pasadena, Calif.
Oct. 1856	Peabody, Andrew Preston	Mar. 19, 1811 – Mar. 11, 1893	Portsmouth, N.H.
Oct. 1891	*Peabody, Endicott	May 30, 1857 – Nov. 17, 1944	Groton, Mass.
Apr. 1867	Peabody, George	Feb. 18, 1795 – Nov. 4, 1869	London, England
Oct. 1865	Peale, Franklin	Oct. 15, 1795 – May 5, 1870	Philadelphia, Pa.
Oct. 1814	Pearson, Joseph	1776 – Oct. 27, 1834	Salisbury, N.C.
1812	Peck, William Dandridge	May 8, 1763 – Oct. 3, 1822	Cambridge, Mass.
Oct. 1956	Peckham, Howard Henry	Jul. 13, 1910 –	Ann Arbor, Mich.
Apr. 1858	Pedro II, Emperor of Brazil	Dec. 2, 1825 – Dec. 5, 1891	Rio de Janeiro, Brazil
Apr. 1882	Peet, Stephen Denison	Dec. 2, 1831 – May 24, 1914	Clinton, Wis.
Oct. 1975	Pell, Claiborne	Nov. 22, 1918 –	Washington, D.C.
Apr. 1930	Pell, John Howland Gibbs	Aug. 9, 1904 –	Fort Ticonderoga, N.Y.
Oct. 1950	Peltz, William Law Learned	May 27, 1882 – Mar. 26, 1961	Albany, N.Y.
Apr. 1910	Penafiel, Antonio	d. ca. 1914	Mexico City, Mexico
Apr. 1935	Pennington, Edgar Legare	Jan. 15, 1891 – Dec. 10, 1951	Ocala, Fla.

* resigned

Oct. 1912	Pennypacker, Samuel Whitaker	Apr. 9, 1843 – Sep. 2, 1916	Pennypacker's Mills, Pa.
Oct. 1879	Perez, Andres Aznar	Jul. 5, 1831 – Jan. 23, 1894	Merida, Yucatan
Apr. 1866	Perley, Ira	Nov. 9, 1799 – Feb. 26, 1874	Concord, N.H.
Apr. 1882	Perry, William Stevens	Jan. 22, 1832 – May 13, 1898	Davenport, Iowa
Oct. 1981	Pessen, Edward	Dec. 31, 1920 –	Brooklyn, N.Y.
Apr. 1932	Peters, Harry Twyford	Aug. 1, 1881 – Jun. 1, 1948	New York, N.Y.
Apr. 1979	Peterson, Hall James	Jun. 4, 1939 –	Petersham, Mass.
Oct. 1983	Peterson, Merrill Daniel	Mar. 31, 1921 –	Charlottesville, Va.
Apr. 1979	Pettit, William Oscar, Jr.	Oct. 27, 1921 –	Worcester, Mass.
Oct. 1912	Pezet, Federico Alfonso	b. Jul. 18, 1859	Washington, D.C.
Apr. 1893	Phelps, Edward John	Jul. 11, 1822 – Mar. 9, 1900	Burlington, Vt.
Oct. 1936	Phillips, James Duncan	Feb. 5, 1876 – Oct. 19, 1954	Topsfield, Mass.
Dec. 1813	Phillips, John	Nov. 26, 1770 – May 23, 1823	Boston, Mass.
Oct. 1949	Phillips, John Marshall	Jan. 2, 1905 – May 7, 1953	New Haven, Conn.
Apr. 1930	Phillips, Stephen Willard	Jan. 9, 1873 – Jul. 6, 1955	Salem, Mass.
Dec. 1813	Phillips, William	Mar. 30, 1750 – May 26, 1827	Boston, Mass.
Dec. 1821	Pickering, John	Feb. 7, 1777 – May 5, 1846	Salem, Mass.
Oct. 1892	Pierce, Edward Lillie	May 29, 1829 – Sep. 5, 1897	Milton, Mass.
Jan. 1815	Pierce, John	Jul. 14, 1773 – Aug. 24, 1849	Brookline, Mass.
Dec. 1813	Pinckney, Charles Cotesworth	Feb. 25, 1746 – Aug. 16, 1825	Charleston, S.C.
Jun. 1814	Pinckney, Thomas	Oct. 23, 1750 – Nov. 2, 1828	Charleston, S.C.
Jun. 1814	Pintard, John	May 18, 1759 – Jun. 21, 1844	New York, N.Y.
Jul. 1815	Pitkin, Timothy	Jan. 21, 1766 – Dec. 18, 1847	Farmington, Conn.
Oct. 1925	Place, Charles Alpheus	Apr. 7, 1866 – Nov. 17, 1940	Lancaster, Mass.
Oct. 1937	Pleasants, J. Hall	Sep. 12, 1873 – Aug. 24, 1957	Baltimore, Md.
Apr. 1914	Plimpton, George Arthur	Jul. 13, 1855 – Jul. 1, 1936	New York, N.Y.
Jul. 1815	Plumer, William	Jun. 25, 1779 – Dec. 22, 1850	Epping, N.H.
Apr. 1985	Poesch, Jessie Jean	May 19, 1922 –	New Orleans, La.
Apr. 1925	Pollard, Alfred William	Aug. 14, 1859 – Mar. 8, 1944	London, England
Jun. 1814	Pomeroy, Samuel Wyllys	d. Jun. 5, 1841	Brighton, Mass.
Oct. 1957	Pomfret, John Edwin	Sep. 21, 1898 – Nov. 26, 1981	San Marino, Calif.
Oct. 1943	Pond, Shepard	Feb. 18, 1889 – May 28, 1945	Winchester, Mass.
Oct. 1877	Poole, William Frederick	Dec. 24, 1821 – Mar. 1, 1894	Chicago, Ill.
Oct. 1874	Poore, Benjamin Perley	Nov. 2, 1820 – May 29, 1887	Newbury, Mass.
Oct. 1970	Porter, Dorothy Burnett	May 25, 1905 –	Washington, D.C.
Apr. 1876	Porter, Edward Griffin	Jan. 24, 1837 – Feb. 5, 1900	Lexington, Mass.
Oct. 1822	Porter, Jacob	Dec. 30, 1783 – Nov. 15, 1846	Plainfield, Mass.

Jul. 1815	Porter, Samuel	Jun. 11, 1760 – Sep. 23, 1825	Greenburgh, Pa.
Apr. 1919	Potter, Alfred Claghorn	Apr. 4, 1867 – Nov. 1, 1940	Cambridge, Mass.
Oct. 1855	Potter, Chandler Eastman	Mar. 7, 1807 – Aug. 3, 1868	Manchester, N.H.
Jul. 1815	Potter, Elisha Reynolds	Nov. 5, 1764 – Sep. 26, 1835	South Kingston, R.I.
Apr. 1898	Powell, John Wesley	Mar. 24, 1834 – Sep. 23, 1902	Washington, D.C.
Apr. 1943	Pratt, Frederick Haven	Jul. 19, 1873 – Jul. 12, 1958	Boston, Mass.
Oct. 1873	Preble, George Henry	Feb. 25, 1816 – Mar. 1, 1885	Portland, Maine
Jun. 1813	Prescott, Samuel Jackson	Mar. 15, 1773 – Feb. 7, 1857	Boston, Mass.
May 1839	Prescott, William Hickling	May 14, 1796 – Jan. 28, 1859	Boston, Mass.
Oct. 1814	Prince, John	Jul. 4, 1751 – Jun. 7, 1836	Salem, Mass.
Apr. 1916	Prince, Lebaron Bradford	Jul. 3, 1840 – Dec. 8, 1922	Santa Fe, N.Mex.
Apr. 1902	*Pritchett, Henry Smith	Apr. 16, 1857 – Aug. 28, 1939	Boston, Mass.
Apr. 1985	Prouty, Richard	Nov. 20, 1912 –	Holden, Mass.
Oct. 1966	Prown, Jules David	Mar. 14, 1930 –	New Haven, Conn.
Apr. 1983	Prucha, Francis Paul	Jan. 4, 1921 –	Chestnut Hill, Mass.
Apr. 1882	Putnam, Frederick Ward	Apr. 16, 1839 – Aug. 14, 1915	Cambridge, Mass.
Oct. 1907	Putnam, Herbert	Sep. 20, 1861 – Aug. 14, 1955	Washington, D.C.
Oct. 1816	Putnam, Samuel	Apr. 13, 1768 – Jul. 3, 1853	Salem, Mass.
Apr. 1951	Putnam, William Hutchinson	Feb. 1, 1878 – Mar. 10, 1958	Hartford, Conn.
Oct. 1914	Quaife, Milo Milton	Oct. 6, 1880 – Sep. 1, 1959	Madison, Wis.
Oct. 1975	Quarles, Benjamin Arthur	Jan. 23, 1904 –	Baltimore, Md.
Apr. 1910	Quevedo, Samuel Alexander Lafone	d. Jun. 18, 1920	La Plata, Argentina
Oct. 1875	Quincy, Edmund	Feb. 1, 1808 – May 17, 1877	Dedham, Mass.
1812	Quincy, Josiah	Feb. 4, 1772 – Jul. 1, 1864	Boston, Mass.
Apr. 1943	Quinn, Arthur Hobson	Feb. 9, 1875 – Oct. 16, 1960	Philadelphia, Pa.
Oct. 1822	Raffles, Thomas Stamford	Jul. 5, 1781 – Jul. 5, 1826	Singapore
Aug. 1820	Rafinesque, Constantine Samuel	Oct. 22, 1783 – Sep. 18, 1840	Lexington, Ky.
May 1836	Rafn, Carl Christian	Jan. 16, 1795 – Oct. 20, 1864	Copenhagen, Denmark
Apr. 1985	Ragen, Brooks Geer	Jul. 6, 1933 –	Seattle, Wash.
Apr. 1862	Ramirez, Jose Fernando	ca. 1812 – Mar. 4, 1871	Mexico City, Mexico
Jun. 1813	Ramsay, David	Apr. 2, 1749 – May 8, 1815	Charleston, S.C.
Jul. 1815	Randolph, John	Jun. 2, 1773 – May 24, 1833	Roanoke, Va.
Oct. 1878	Rau, Charles	1826 – Jul. 25, 1887	Washington, D.C.
Apr. 1879	Rawson, Guillermo	1821 – Feb. 2, 1890	Buenos Aires, Argentina

* resigned

Apr. 1971	Ray, Gordon Norton	Sep. 8, 1915 – Dec. 15, 1986	New York, N.Y.
Jun. 1814	Reed, John	Sep. 2, 1781 – Nov. 25, 1860	Yarmouth, Mass.
Apr. 1981	Reese, William Sherman	Jul. 29, 1955 –	New Haven, Conn.
Apr. 1987	Reingold, Nathan	Mar. 23, 1927 –	Washington, D.C.
Apr. 1982	Reps, John William	Nov. 25, 1921 –	Ithaca, N.Y.
Oct. 1885	Reynolds, Grindall	Dec. 22, 1822 – Sep. 30, 1894	Concord, Mass.
Apr. 1971	Rhoads, James Berton	Sep. 17, 1928 –	Washington, D.C.
Oct. 1816	Rhodes, Dudley Woodbridge	d. Oct. 16, 1840	Zanesville, Ohio
Oct. 1900	Rhodes, James Ford	May 1, 1848 – Jan. 22, 1927	Boston, Mass.
Apr. 1919	Ricci, Seymour De	d. Dec. 26, 1942	Paris, France
Oct. 1954	Riccius, Hermann Porter	Oct. 4, 1883 – Feb. 11, 1965	Worcester, Mass.
Apr. 1938	Rice, Albert White	Jan. 24, 1883 – Aug. 8, 1965	Worcester, Mass.
Oct. 1906	Rice, Franklin Pierce	Jul. 29, 1852 – Jan. 4, 1919	Worcester, Mass.
Jul. 1815	Rice, John Holt	Nov. 28, 1777 – Sep. 3, 1831	Richmond, Va.
Oct. 1967	Rice, Mary Gage	Nov. 29, 1901 – Nov. 23, 1977	Worcester, Mass.
Apr. 1885	Rice, William Whitney	Mar. 7, 1826 – Mar. 1, 1896	Worcester, Mass.
Apr. 1965	Rich, Daniel Catton	Apr. 16, 1904 – Oct. 15, 1976	Worcester, Mass.
Oct. 1834	Rich, Obadiah	Nov. 25, 1777 – Jan. 20, 1850	London, England
Jun. 1814	Richards, James	Oct. 29, 1767 – Aug. 2, 1843	Newark, N.J.
Oct. 1973	Richardson, Edgar Preston	Dec. 2, 1902 – Mar. 27, 1985	Philadelphia, Pa.
Oct. 1819	Richardson, William Merchant	Jan. 4, 1774 – Mar. 23, 1838	Portsmouth, N.H.
Apr. 1948	Richmond, Carleton Rubira	Feb. 13, 1887 – Dec. 13, 1975	Milton, Mass.
Apr. 1982	Ridge, Martin	May 7, 1923 –	San Marino, Calif.
Oct. 1951	Riley, Stephen Thomas	Dec. 28, 1908 –	Boston, Mass.
Oct. 1982	Ring, Betty Ruth	Mar. 18, 1923 –	Houston, Tex.
Oct. 1973	Riznik, Barnes	Jul. 21, 1931 –	Sturbridge, Mass.
May 1838	Rizo-Rangabe, Alexander	ca. 1810 – Jan. 28, 1892	Athens, Greece
Oct. 1857	Robbins, Chandler	Feb. 14, 1810 – Sep. 11, 1882	Boston, Mass.
Dec. 1813	Robbins, Edward Hutchinson	Feb. 18, 1758 – Dec. 29, 1829	Milton, Mass.
Jul. 1815	Robbins, Samuel Prince	Apr. 20, 1777 – Sep. 2, 1823	Marietta, Ohio
Oct. 1815	Robbins, Thomas	Aug. 11, 1777 – Sep. 13, 1856	East Windsor, Conn.
Oct. 1963	Robbins, Wallace Woodsome	Oct. 16, 1910 –	Worcester, Mass.
Apr. 1987	Roberts, Eugene Leslie, Jr.	Jun. 15, 1932 –	Philadelphia, Pa.
Oct. 1924	Robertson, James Alexander	Aug. 19, 1873 – Mar. 20, 1939	Deland, Fla.
Oct. 1837	Robertson, John Jacob	d. Oct. 6, 1881	Syra, Greece
Dec. 1821	Robertson, Thomas Bolling	Feb. 27, 1779 – Oct. 5, 1828	New Orleans, La.
Oct. 1920	Robinson, Fred Norris	Apr. 4, 1871 – Jul. 21, 1966	Cambridge, Mass.

Apr. 1891	*Robinson, George Dexter	Jan. 20, 1834 – Feb. 22, 1896	Chicopee, Mass.
Oct. 1838	Rochette, Raoul	Mar. 9, 1790 – Jul. 3, 1854	Paris, France
Apr. 1923	Rockwood, George Ichabod	Jan. 13, 1868 – Oct. 30, 1959	Worcester, Mass.
Apr. 1976	Roderick, Natalie Johnson Allen	Jun. 25, 1913 –	Worcester, Mass.
Apr. 1910	Rodriguez, Jose Carlos	ca. 1844 – Jun. 29, 1923	Rio De Janeiro, Brazil
Oct. 1917	Rodway, James	1848 – Nov. 27, 1926	Georgetown, British Guiana
Apr. 1941	Roelker, William Greene	Apr. 9, 1886 – May 29, 1953	Providence, R.I.
Apr. 1980	Rogers, George Calvin	Jun. 15, 1922 –	Columbia, S.C.
Apr. 1882	Rogers, Horatio	May 18, 1824 – Nov. 12, 1904	Providence, R.I.
Apr. 1976	Rogers, Rutherford David	Jun. 22, 1915 – Jan. 28, 1985	New Haven, Conn.
Oct. 1924	Roosevelt, Franklin Delano	Jan. 30, 1882 – Apr. 12, 1945	Hyde Park, N.Y.
Apr. 1918	Roosevelt, Theodore	Oct. 27, 1858 – Jan. 6, 1919	Oyster Bay, N.Y.
Oct. 1975	Rose, Willie Lee	May 18, 1927 –	Baltimore, Md.
Oct. 1927	Rosenbach, Abraham Simon Wolf	Jul. 22, 1876 – Jul. 1, 1952	Philadelphia, Pa.
Apr. 1984	Rosenberg, Charles Ernest	Nov. 11, 1936 –	Philadelphia, Pa.
Apr. 1972	Rosenthal, Samuel Robert	Jun. 6, 1899 –	Chicago, Ill.
Apr. 1954	Rosenwald, Lessing Julius	Feb. 10, 1891 – Jun. 24, 1979	Jenkintown, Pa.
Jul. 1815	Ross, James	Jul. 12, 1762 – Nov. 27, 1847	Pittsburgh, Pa.
Oct. 1837	Ross, Ludwig	d. Aug. 6, 1859	Athens, Greece
Apr. 1882	Rossi, Giovanni Battista De		Rome, Italy
Oct. 1956	Rossiter, Clinton	Sep. 18, 1917 – Jul. 10, 1970	Ithaca, N.Y.
Oct. 1899	Rotch, Abbott Lawrence	Jan. 6, 1861 – Apr. 7, 1912	Boston, Mass.
Apr. 1976	Ruffner, Frederick Gale, Jr.	Aug. 6, 1926 –	Grosse Pointe, Mich.
Oct. 1908	Rugg, Arthur Prentice	Aug. 20, 1862 – Jun. 12, 1938	Worcester, Mass.
Apr. 1948	Rugg, Charles Belcher	Jan. 20, 1890 – Nov. 25, 1962	Boston, Mass.
Apr. 1976	Rumford, Beatrix Tyson	Jun. 16, 1939 –	Williamsburg, Va.
Jun. 1814	Rush, Richard	Aug. 29, 1780 – Jul. 30, 1859	Washington, D.C.
Oct. 1930	Rusk, Ralph Leslie	Jul. 11, 1888 – Jun. 30, 1962	New York, N.Y.
1812	Russell, Benjamin	Sep. 13, 1761 – Jan. 4, 1845	Boston, Mass.
Oct. 1900	Russell, Elias Harlow	Dec. 27, 1836 – Apr. 3, 1917	Worcester, Mass.
Oct. 1977	Rutland, Robert Allen	Oct. 1, 1922 –	Charlottesville, Va.
Apr. 1984	Ryan, Mary Patricia	Jan. 12, 1945 –	Irvine, Calif.
Apr. 1982	Ryskamp, Charles Andrew	Oct. 21, 1928 –	New York, N.Y.
Dec. 1821	Sacy, Antoine I. Silvestre De	Sep. 21, 1758 – Feb. 20, 1838	Paris, France
Apr. 1977	Sadik, Marvin Sherwood	Jun. 27, 1932 –	Washington, D.C.

* resigned

Apr. 1978	Saffron, Morris Harold	Jan. 28, 1905 –	New York, N.Y.
Oct. 1867	Sainsbury, William Noel	Jul. 7, 1825 – Mar. 9, 1895	London, England
Oct. 1863	Salisbury, Charles Babcock	Aug. 20, 1821 – Aug. 21, 1888	Little York, N.Y.
Oct. 1861	Salisbury, Edward Elbridge	Apr. 6, 1814 – Feb. 5, 1901	New Haven, Conn.
Apr. 1862	Salisbury, James Henry	Oct. 13, 1823 – Aug. 23, 1905	Newark, Ohio
Oct. 1840	Salisbury, Stephen	Mar. 8, 1798 – Aug. 24, 1884	Worcester, Mass.
Oct. 1863	Salisbury, Stephen, Jr.	Mar. 31, 1835 – Nov. 16, 1905	Worcester, Mass.
Apr. 1914	Salley, Alexander Samuel	Jun. 16, 1871 – Feb. 19, 1961	Columbia, S.C.
Dec. 1813	Sanders, Daniel Clarke	May 3, 1768 – Oct. 18, 1850	Burlington, Vt.
Apr. 1961	Sandrof, Ivan	Jul. 12, 1911 – Feb. 1, 1979	Worcester, Mass.
Dec. 1813	Sargent, Epes	Nov. 2, 1748 – Apr. 18, 1822	Boston, Mass.
Oct. 1860	Sargent, Joseph	Dec. 31, 1815 – Oct. 13, 1888	Worcester, Mass.
Dec. 1813	Sargent, Winthrop	May 1, 1753 – Jun. 3, 1820	Natchez, Miss.
Oct. 1859	Sargent, Winthrop	Sep. 23, 1825 – May 18, 1870	Philadelphia, Pa.
Apr. 1982	Sargisson, Duane Thomas	Apr. 11, 1934 –	Worcester, Mass.
Oct. 1929	Savage, Maxwell	Jun. 13, 1876 – Nov. 4, 1948	Worcester, Mass.
Jun. 1814	Savage, Samuel	Aug. 11, 1748 – Jun. 28, 1831	Barnstable, Mass.
Oct. 1973	Savelle, Maxwell	Jan. 8, 1896 – Aug. 13, 1979	Chicago, Ill.
Oct. 1908	Saville, Marshall Howard	Jun. 24, 1867 – May 7, 1935	New York, N.Y.
Oct. 1945	Sawitzky, William	Nov. 30, 1879 – Feb. 2, 1947	Stamford, Conn.
Apr. 1946	Sawyer, Charles Henry	Oct. 20, 1906 –	Worcester, Mass.
Apr. 1966	Sawyer, John Edward	May 5, 1917 –	Williamstown, Mass.
Oct. 1938	Scheide, John Hinsdale	Aug. 9, 1875 – Sep. 29, 1942	Titusville, Pa.
Oct. 1966	Scheide, William Hurd	Jan. 6, 1914 –	Princeton, N.J.
Oct. 1984	Schiller, Justin Galland	Sep. 10, 1943 –	New York, N.Y.
Oct. 1838	Schinas, Constantine Demetrius		Athens, Greece
May 1836	Schlegel, August Wilhelm	Sep. 8, 1767 – May 12, 1845	Copenhagen, Denmark
Apr. 1939	Schlesinger, Arthur Meier	Feb. 27, 1888 – Oct. 30, 1965	Cambridge, Mass.
Apr. 1881	Schliemann, Heinrich	Jan. 6, 1822 – Dec. 26, 1890	Athens, Greece
Apr. 1977	Schlosser, Leonard Benjamin	Mar. 28, 1925 –	Greenwich, Conn.
Dec. 1821	Schoolcraft, Henry Rowe	Mar. 28, 1793 – Dec. 10, 1864	Detroit, Mich.
Oct. 1907	Schouler, James	Mar. 20, 1839 – Apr. 16, 1920	Intervale, N.H.
Apr. 1984	Schwartz, Seymour Ira	Jan. 22, 1928 –	Pittsford, N.Y.
Oct. 1927	Scofield, William Bacon	Feb. 8, 1864 – Jan. 22, 1930	Worcester, Mass.
Oct. 1979	Scott, Anne Firor	Apr. 24, 1921 –	Durham, N.C.
Apr. 1947	Scott, Donald	Jun. 4, 1879 – Apr. 4, 1967	Cambridge, Mass.
Jun. 1814	Scudder, David	ca. 1762 – Jan. 17, 1819	Barnstable, Mass.

Apr. 1974	Seelye, John Douglas	Jan. 1, 1931 –	Hillsborough, N.C.
Jul. 1825	Selden, George	d. Apr. 28, 1835	Meadville, Pa.
Apr. 1910	Seler, Edward	Dec. 5, 1849 – Nov. 23, 1922	Berlin, Germany
Jun. 1814	Sever, James	Nov. 3, 1761 – Dec. 16, 1845	Kingston, Mass.
Oct. 1814	Sewall, David	Oct. 7, 1735 – Oct. 22, 1825	York, Maine
Apr. 1919	Sewall, Harold Marsh	Jan. 3, 1860 – Oct. 28, 1924	Bath, Maine
Jun. 1814	Sewall, Samuel	Dec. 11, 1757 – Jun. 8, 1814	Marblehead, Mass.
Oct. 1815	Sewell, Stephen	d. Jun., 1832	Montreal, Que.
Apr. 1930	Seybolt, Robert Francis	Feb. 25, 1888 – Feb. 5, 1951	Urbana, Ill.
Apr. 1966	Seymour, Forrest Wilson	Jul. 10, 1905 – Oct. 3, 1983	Worcester, Mass.
Oct. 1936	Seymour, George Dudley	Oct. 5, 1859 – Jan. 21, 1945	New Haven, Conn.
Apr. 1980	Shannon, William Vincent	Aug. 24, 1927 –	Washington, D.C.
Oct. 1831	Shattuck, Lemuel	Oct. 15, 1793 – Jan. 17, 1859	Concord, Mass.
Oct. 1893	Shaw, Albert	Jul. 23, 1857 – Jun. 25, 1947	New York, N.Y.
Jan. 1817	Shaw, Charles	1782 – Nov. 1, 1828	Boston, Mass.
Oct. 1855	Shaw, Lemuel	Jan. 9, 1781 – Mar. 30, 1861	Boston, Mass.
Apr. 1959	Shaw, Ralph Robert	May 18, 1907 – Oct. 14, 1972	New Brunswick, N.J.
Apr. 1919	Shaw, Robert Kendall	Jul. 18, 1871 – Jul. 3, 1956	Worcester, Mass.
1812	Shaw, William Smith	Aug. 12, 1778 – Apr. 25, 1826	Boston, Mass.
Jul. 1815	Sheafe, James	Nov. 16, 1755 – Dec. 5, 1829	Portsmouth, N.H.
Oct. 1814	Sheffey, Daniel	1770 – Dec. 3, 1830	Wytheville, Va.
Jun. 1813	Sheldon, William	d. Jun. 28, 1822	Jamaica, West Indies
Apr. 1920	Shepley, George Leander	Oct. 11, 1854 – Aug. 3, 1924	Providence, R.I.
Apr. 1818	Sherman, David Austin	Dec. 10, 1781 – Dec. 16, 1843	Knoxville, Tenn.
Oct. 1966	Sherman, Stuart Capen	Oct. 30, 1916 – Apr. 8, 1983	Providence, R.I.
Oct. 1844	Sherwood, Oliver Henry		Toronto, Ont.
Apr. 1884	Shiels, Arturo	1835 – Nov. 23, 1886	Campeche, Mexico
Apr. 1937	Shipton, Clifford Kenyon	Aug. 5, 1902 – Dec. 4, 1973	Shirley, Mass.
Oct. 1982	Shirley, Betsey Beinecke	Oct. 2, 1919 –	Bernardsville, N.J.
Apr. 1948	Shoemaker, Alfred Lewis		Reading, Pa.
Apr. 1881	Short, John Thomas	May 1, 1850 – Nov. 11, 1883	Columbus, Ohio
Oct. 1923	Shortt, Adam	Nov. 24, 1859 – Jan. 14, 1931	Ottawa, Ont.
Oct. 1947	Shryock, Richard Harrison	Mar. 29, 1893 – Jan. 30, 1972	Philadelphia, Pa.
Oct. 1849	Shurtleff, Nathaniel Bradstreet	Jun. 29, 1810 – Oct. 17, 1874	Boston, Mass.
Oct. 1813	Shurtleff, Roswell	Aug. 29, 1773 – Feb. 4, 1861	Hanover, N.H.
Oct. 1974	Shy, John Willard	Mar. 23, 1931 –	Ann Arbor, Mich.
Apr. 1986	Siebert, Frank Thomas	Apr. 2, 1912 –	Old Town, Maine
Oct. 1925	Siebert, Wilbur Henry	Aug. 30, 1866 – Sep. 2, 1961	Columbus, Ohio

Sep. 1813	Silliman, Benjamin	Aug. 8, 1779 – Nov. 24, 1864	New Haven, Conn.
Apr. 1977	Silsby, Herbert Trafton, II	Feb. 8, 1925 –	Ellsworth, Maine
Oct. 1951	Silver, Rollo Gabriel	Jun. 27, 1909 –	Boston, Mass.
Oct. 1977	Silverman, Kenneth Eugene	Feb. 5, 1936 –	New York, N.Y.
Apr. 1965	Simpson, Alan	Jul. 23, 1912 –	Poughkeepsie, N.Y.
Apr. 1931	Sinclair, Joseph Henry	Jul. 18, 1879 – May 24, 1946	New York, N.Y.
Oct. 1930	Sioussat, St. George Leakin	Mar. 13, 1878 – Aug. 31, 1960	Philadelphia, Pa.
Oct. 1948	Sizer, Theodore	Mar. 19, 1892 – Jun. 21, 1967	Bethany, Conn.
Apr. 1937	Skiff, Frederick Woodward	Aug. 12, 1868 – Mar. 15, 1947	Portland, Oreg.
Apr. 1928	Skinner, Joseph Allen	May 20, 1862 – Sep. 6, 1946	Holyoke, Mass.
Oct. 1977	Sklar, Kathryn Kish	Dec. 26, 1939 –	Los Angeles, Calif.
Apr. 1981	Skramstad, Harold Kenneth, Jr.	Jun. 3, 1941 –	Dearborn, Mich.
Oct. 1910	Sloane, William Milligan	Nov. 12, 1850 – Sep. 11, 1928	New York, N.Y.
Oct. 1986	Slotkin, Richard Sidney	Nov. 8, 1942 –	Middletown, Conn.
Apr. 1876	Smith, Charles Card	Mar. 27, 1827 – Mar. 20, 1918	Boston, Mass.
Jan. 1819	Smith, David	Oct. 2, 1785 – Feb. 3, 1865	Columbus, Ohio
Oct. 1893	Smith, Goldwin	Aug. 23, 1823 – Jun. 7, 1910	Toronto, Ont.
Oct. 1975	*Smith, Henry Nash	Sep. 29, 1906 – May 30, 1986	Berkeley, Calif.
Dec. 1813	Smith, Isaac	May 7, 1749 – Sep. 30, 1829	Boston, Mass.
Oct. 1972	Smith, James Morton	May 28, 1919 –	Madison, Wis.
Jun. 1814	Smith, Jeremiah	Nov. 29, 1759 – Sep. 21, 1842	Exeter, N.H.
Dec. 1813	Smith, John Cotton	Feb. 12, 1765 – Dec. 7, 1845	Sharon, Conn.
Apr. 1909	Smith, Justin Harvey	Jan. 13, 1857 – Mar. 21, 1930	Hanover, N.H.
Oct. 1973	Smith, Lawrence Meredith Clemson	Oct. 4, 1902 – Aug. 10, 1975	Germantown, Pa.
Oct. 1980	Smith, Merritt Roe	Nov. 14, 1940 –	Cambridge, Mass.
Jul. 1815	Smith, Thomas		Franklin, Pa.
Oct. 1862	Smith, Thomas Buckingham	1810 – Jan. 6, 1871	St. Augustine, Fla.
Apr. 1974	Smith, Wilfred Irvin	May 20, 1919 –	Ottawa, Ont.
Oct. 1867	Smith, William Addison	Mar. 2, 1824 – Sep. 25, 1913	Worcester, Mass.
Apr. 1871	Smucker, Isaac	Dec. 14, 1807 – Jan. 31, 1894	Newark, Ohio
Apr. 1870	Smythe, Egbert Coffin	Aug. 24, 1829 – Apr. 12, 1904	Andover, Mass.
Jun. 1813	Snelling, Nathaniel Greenwood	d. Sep. 7, 1858	Boston, Mass.
Oct. 1978	Solomon, Barbara Miller	Feb. 12, 1919 –	Cambridge, Mass.
Oct. 1814	Sorrel, J.		Attacapas, La.
Oct. 1822	Southey, Robert	Aug. 12, 1774 – Mar. 21, 1843	Keswick, England
Jun. 1814	Spafford, Horatio Gates	Feb. 18, 1778 – Aug. 7, 1832	Albany, N.Y.

* resigned

Oct. 1814	Spalding, Lyman	Jun. 5, 1775 – Oct. 21, 1821	New York, N.Y.
Apr. 1936	Spalding, Philip Leffingwell	Jun. 27, 1871 – Dec. 4, 1938	Boston, Mass.
Oct. 1827	Sparks, Jared	May 10, 1789 – Mar. 14, 1866	Boston, Mass.
Oct. 1962	Spawn, Willman	May 29, 1920 –	Philadelphia, Pa.
Oct. 1982	Spear, Hope Hartwell	Mar. 22, 1924 –	Worcester, Mass.
Jul. 1815	Spear, William	d. Apr. 28, 1829	Greenburgh, Pa.
Oct. 1953	Spencer, Rae Mac Collum	Jul. 9, 1887 – Mar. 17, 1972	Worcester, Mass.
Oct. 1962	Spiller, Robert Ernest	Nov. 13, 1896 –	Swarthmore, Pa.
Oct. 1926	Spinden, Herbert Joseph	Aug. 16, 1879 – Oct. 23, 1967	Cambridge, Mass.
Apr. 1958	Spinney, Frank Oakman	Jan. 14, 1909 –	Sturbridge, Mass.
Jun. 1814	Spooner, Nathaniel	ca. 1759 – Feb. 20, 1826	Plymouth, Mass.
May 1846	Sprague, William Buell	Oct. 16, 1795 – May 7, 1876	Albany, N.Y.
Apr. 1982	Stam, David Harry	Jul. 11, 1935 –	Pelham, N.Y.
Oct. 1972	Stampp, Kenneth Milton	Jul. 12, 1912 –	Berkeley, Calif.
Oct. 1924	Stanard, William Glover	Oct. 2, 1858 – May 6, 1933	Richmond, Va.
Oct. 1816	Stanhope, Charles	Aug. 3, 1753 – Dec. 15, 1816	London, England
Dec. 1813	Staniford, Daniel	ca. 1765 – Sep. 22, 1820	Boston, Mass.
Apr. 1878	Staples, Hamilton Barclay	Feb. 14, 1829 – Aug. 2, 1891	Worcester, Mass.
Oct. 1855	Staples, William Reed	Oct. 10, 1798 – Oct. 19, 1868	Providence, R.I.
Oct. 1957	Stark, Lewis Morgrage	Jan. 8, 1908 –	New York, N.Y.
Oct. 1895	Stearns, Ezra Scollay	Sep. 1, 1838 – Mar. 9, 1915	Concord, N.H.
Apr. 1936	Stearns, Foster	Jul. 29, 1881 – Jun. 4, 1956	Hancock, N.H.
Apr. 1951	Stearns, Raymond Phineas	Jan. 11, 1904 – Nov. 15, 1970	Urbana, Ill.
Oct. 1891	Stebbins, Calvin	Apr. 22, 1837 – Dec. 30, 1921	Worcester, Mass.
Apr. 1984	Stebbins, Theodore Ellis, Jr.	Aug. 11, 1938 –	Brookline, Mass.
Oct. 1813	Stedman, William	Jan. 21, 1765 – Aug. 31, 1831	Worcester, Mass.
Oct. 1972	Steele, Richard Charles	May 13, 1917 –	Worcester, Mass.
Oct. 1984	Stegner, Wallace Earle	Feb. 18, 1909 –	Los Altos, Calif.
Oct. 1913	Steiner, Bernard Christian	Aug. 13, 1867 – Jan. 12, 1926	Baltimore, Md.
Oct. 1901	Stephen, Leslie	Nov. 28, 1832 – Feb. 22, 1904	London, England
Oct. 1920	Stephenson, Nathaniel Wright	Jul. 10, 1867 – Jan. 17, 1935	Charleston, S.C.
Oct. 1923	Stetson, John Batterson	Oct. 14, 1884 – Nov. 15, 1952	Elkins Park, Pa.
Oct. 1896	Stevens, Benjamin Franklin	Feb. 19, 1833 – Mar. 5, 1902	London, England
Apr. 1854	Stevens, Henry	Aug. 24, 1819 – Feb. 28, 1886	London, England
Oct. 1923	Stevens, Henry Newton		London, England
Apr. 1908	Stevenson, Edward Luther	Oct. 18, 1858 – Jul. 16, 1944	New Brunswick, N.J.
Oct. 1966	Stinehour, Roderick Douglas	Mar. 21, 1925 –	Lunenburg, Vt.
Oct. 1945	Stobbs, George Russell	Feb. 7, 1877 – Dec. 23, 1966	Worcester, Mass.

Apr. 1971	Stobbs, Russell Murdock	Aug. 7, 1907 – Mar. 12, 1975	Worcester, Mass.
Jul. 1815	Stockton, Richard	Apr. 17, 1764 – Mar. 7, 1828	Princeton, N.J.
Oct. 1865	Stoddard, Elijah Brigham	Jun. 5, 1826 – Sep. 25, 1903	Worcester, Mass.
Apr. 1927	Stoddard, Harry Galpin	Sep. 13, 1873 – May 21, 1969	Worcester, Mass.
Apr. 1985	Stoddard, Helen Estabrook	Sep. 8, 1904 –	Worcester, Mass.
Oct. 1963	Stoddard, Robert Waring	Jan. 22, 1906 – Dec. 14, 1984	Worcester, Mass.
Oct. 1965	Stoddard, Roger Eliot	Dec. 2, 1935 –	Cambridge, Mass.
Oct. 1919	Stokes, Isaac Newton Phelps	Apr. 11, 1867 – Dec. 18, 1944	New York, N.Y.
Apr. 1869	Stone, Edwin Martin	Apr. 29, 1805 – Dec. 15, 1883	Providence, R.I.
Apr. 1818	Stone, Ethan		Cincinnati, Ohio
Apr. 1931	Stone, Wilbur Macey	Nov. 30, 1862 – Dec. 21, 1941	New York, N.Y.
Jun. 1814	Story, Joseph	Sep. 18, 1779 – Sep. 10, 1845	Salem, Mass.
Apr. 1954	Stout, George Leslie	Oct. 5, 1897 – Jul. 1, 1978	Worcester, Mass.
Apr. 1865	Stowe, Calvin Ellis	Apr. 26, 1802 – Aug. 22, 1886	Hartford, Conn.
May 1846	Strachan, John	Apr. 12, 1778 – Nov. 1, 1867	Toronto, Ont.
Apr. 1968	Strauss, Herbert Ranger	Jul. 27, 1899 – Feb. 11, 1974	Chicago, Ill.
Apr. 1971	Streeter, Frank Sherwin		New York, N.Y.
Oct. 1969	Streeter, Henry Schofield	May 2, 1920 –	Wenham, Mass.
Apr. 1933	Streeter, Thomas Winthrop	Jul. 20, 1883 – Jun. 12, 1965	New York, N.Y.
Dec. 1813	Strong, Caleb	Jan. 9, 1745 – Nov. 7, 1819	Northampton, Mass.
Sep. 1813	Strong, Lewis	Jun. 9, 1785 – Oct. 25, 1863	Northampton, Mass.
Oct. 1893	Stubbs, William	Jun. 21, 1825 – Apr. 22, 1901	Oxford, England
Apr. 1910	Suarez, Federico Gonzales	Apr. 15, 1844 – Dec. 1, 1917	Quito, Ecuador
Oct. 1983	Sudler, Barbara Welch	Apr. 20, 1925 –	Denver, Colo.
Oct. 1982	Sullivan, William Francis	May 22, 1927 –	Worcester, Mass.
Apr. 1975	Sulzberger, Arthur Ochs	Feb. 5, 1926 –	New York, N.Y.
May 1843	Sumner, Charles	Jan. 6, 1811 – Mar. 11, 1874	Boston, Mass.
Jun. 1814	*Sumner, Charles Pinckney	b. 1776	Boston, Mass.
Jun. 1813	Sumner, Joseph	Jan. 19, 1739 – Dec. 9, 1824	Shrewsbury, Mass.
Oct. 1953	Swan, Bradford Fuller	Oct. 27, 1907 – Feb. 20, 1976	Providence, R.I.
Oct. 1853	Sweetser, Seth	Mar. 15, 1807 – Mar. 24, 1878	Worcester, Mass.
Oct. 1936	Swem, Earl Gregg	Dec. 29, 1870 – Apr. 12, 1965	Williamsburg, Va.
Oct. 1840	Swords, James	Jun. 18, 1765 – Sep. 17, 1846	New York, N.Y.
Oct. 1876	Taft, Alphonzo	Nov. 5, 1810 – May 2, 1891	Cincinnati, Ohio
Oct. 1820	Taft, Bezaleel, Jr.	Sep. 8, 1780 – Jul. 16, 1846	Uxbridge, Mass.
Oct. 1884	Taft, Henry Walbridge	Nov. 13, 1818 – Sep. 22, 1904	Pittsfield, Mass.
Oct. 1912	Taft, William Howard	Sep. 15, 1857 – Mar. 8, 1930	Washington, D.C.
Oct. 1981	Tanenbaum, Charles Joseph	Oct. 20, 1914 –	New York, N.Y.
Apr. 1965	Tanis, James Robert	Jun. 26, 1928 –	New Haven, Conn.

* resigned

Jul. 1825	Tannehill, Wilkins	Mar. 4, 1787 – Jun. 2, 1858	Nashville, Tenn.
Oct. 1970	Tanselle, George Thomas	Jan. 29, 1934 –	Madison, Wis.
Oct. 1975	Tate, Thaddeus Wilbur, Jr.	May 27, 1924 –	Williamsburg, Va.
Apr. 1955	Tate, Vernon Dale	Jan. 3, 1909 –	Hingham, Mass.
Oct. 1976	Tatham, David Frederick	Nov. 29, 1932 –	Syracuse, N.Y.
Apr. 1932	Tatman, Charles Taylor	Dec. 16, 1871 – Dec. 23, 1945	Worcester, Mass.
Apr. 1864	Taylor, Alexander Smith	Apr. 16, 1817 – Jul. 27, 1876	San Francisco, Calif.
Apr. 1912	Taylor, Charles Henry	Oct. 2, 1867 – May 18, 1941	Boston, Mass.
Oct. 1926	Taylor, Forrest Waldo	Jun. 4, 1865 – Apr. 16, 1951	Worcester, Mass.
Apr. 1956	Taylor, Francis Henry	Apr. 23, 1903 – Nov. 22, 1957	Worcester, Mass.
Apr. 1890	Taylor, Hannis	Sep. 12, 1851 – Dec. 26, 1922	Mobile, Ala.
Apr. 1972	Taylor, Robert Hill	Sep. 12, 1908 – May 5, 1985	Princeton, N.J.
Apr. 1977	Taylor, Robert Joseph	Sep. 14, 1917 –	Boston, Mass.
Apr. 1973	Taylor, William Davis	Apr. 2, 1908 –	Westwood, Mass.
Oct. 1980	Taylor, William Osgood	Jul. 19, 1932 –	Boston, Mass.
Oct. 1977	Teagle, Frank Henry, Jr.	Feb. 26, 1914 –	Woodstock, Vt.
Apr. 1897	Temple, Frederick	Nov. 30, 1821 – Dec. 23, 1902	Canterbury, England
Jul. 1815	Tenney, Samuel	Nov. 27, 1748 – Feb. 6, 1816	Exeter, N.H.
Oct. 1814	Thacher, George	Apr. 12, 1754 – Apr. 6, 1824	Biddeford, Maine
Jun. 1814	*Thacher, James	Feb. 14, 1754 – Aug. 26, 1844	Plymouth, Mass.
Dec. 1813	Thacher, Peter Oxenbridge	Dec. 22, 1776 – Feb. 22, 1843	Boston, Mass.
Jun. 1814	Thaxter, Caleb	Apr. 18, 1751 – Nov. 12, 1828	Hingham, Mass.
Apr. 1927	Thayer, Charles Martin	Dec. 4, 1867 – Nov. 27, 1932	Worcester, Mass.
Apr. 1866	Thayer, Nathaniel	Sep. 11, 1808 – Mar. 7, 1883	Boston, Mass.
Apr. 1919	Thayer, William Roscoe	Jan. 16, 1859 – Sep. 7, 1923	Cambridge, Mass.
Apr. 1901	Thomas, Allen Clapp	Dec. 26, 1846 – Dec. 15, 1920	Haverford, Pa.
Oct. 1840	Thomas, Benjamin Franklin	Feb. 12, 1813 – Sep. 27, 1878	Worcester, Mass.
Oct. 1881	Thomas, Edward Isaiah	Nov. 19, 1833 – Dec. 25, 1890	Brookline, Mass.
Apr. 1917	Thomas, Isaac Rand	Oct. 5, 1864 – Oct. 3, 1954	Boston, Mass.
1812	Thomas, Isaiah	Jan. 19, 1749 – Apr. 4, 1831	Worcester, Mass.
1812	Thomas, Isaiah, Jr.	Sep. 5, 1773 – Jun. 25, 1819	Worcester, Mass.
Oct. 1831	Thomas, Isaiah	Nov. 9, 1805 – Feb., 1862	Cincinnati, Ohio
Jun. 1814	Thomas, Joshua	ca. 1751 – Jan. 10, 1821	Plymouth, Mass.
Oct. 1960	Thomas, Milton Halsey	Feb. 3, 1903 – Jul. 7, 1977	Princeton, N.J.
Oct. 1850	Thomas, William	Apr. 11, 1808 – Jun. 19, 1872	Boston, Mass.
Apr. 1919	Thomas, William	Sep. 5, 1853 – Oct. 18, 1936	San Francisco, Calif.
Dec. 1813	Thompson, Abraham Rand	Mar. 20, 1781 – May 11, 1866	Charlestown, Mass.
Apr. 1878	Thompson, Charles Oliver	Sep. 25, 1836 – Mar. 17, 1885	Worcester, Mass.
Oct. 1933	Thompson, Eben Francis	Jan. 29, 1859 – Dec. 2, 1939	Worcester, Mass.

* resigned

Apr. 1887	Thompson, Edward Herbert	Sep. 28, 1857 – May 11, 1935	Merida, Yucatan
Jan. 1819	Thompson, John	d. Dec. 2, 1842	Chillicothe, Ohio
Oct. 1814	Thompson, Jonathan	d. Sep., 1823	Natchez, Miss.
Dec. 1813	Thomson, Charles	Nov. 29, 1729 – Aug. 16, 1824	Philadelphia, Pa.
Apr. 1855	Thornton, John Wingate	Aug. 12, 1818 – Jun. 6, 1878	Boston, Mass.
Oct. 1966	Thorp, Willard	Apr. 20, 1899 –	Princeton, N.J.
Oct. 1969	Thorpe, James	Aug. 17, 1915 –	San Marino, Calif.
Oct. 1916	Thruston, Rogers Clark Ballard	Nov. 6, 1858 – Dec. 30, 1946	Louisville, Ky.
Apr. 1892	Thwaites, Rueben Gold	May 15, 1853 – Oct. 22, 1913	Madison, Wis.
Oct. 1855	Tiffany, Pardon Dexter	Nov. 18, 1812 – Feb. 14, 1861	Worcester, Mass.
Oct. 1814	Tilden, Joseph	Jun. 17, 1779 – Jul. 28, 1853	Boston, Mass.
Oct. 1816	Tilghman, William	Aug. 12, 1756 – Apr. 29, 1827	Philadelphia, Pa.
Apr. 1907	Tillinghast, Caleb Benjamin	Apr. 3, 1843 – Apr. 28, 1909	Boston, Mass.
Jun. 1814	Tillinghast, Nicholas	Jan. 24, 1767 – Apr. 24, 1818	Taunton, Mass.
Apr. 1980	Tilton, Eleanor Marguerite	Aug. 20, 1913 –	New York, N.Y.
Oct. 1986	Tilton, Sumner B., Jr.	Feb. 25, 1938 –	Worcester, Mass.
Apr. 1932	Tinker, Edward Larocque	Sep. 12, 1881 – Jul. 6, 1968	New York, N.Y.
Oct. 1820	Todd, Thomas	Jan. 23, 1765 – Feb. 7, 1826	Frankfort, N.Y.
Apr. 1967	Tolles, Frederick Barnes	Apr. 18, 1915 – Apr. 18, 1975	Swarthmore, Pa.
Jun. 1814	Tompkins, Daniel D.	Jun. 21, 1774 – Jun. 11, 1825	New York, N.Y.
Apr. 1885	Toppan, Robert Noxon	Oct. 17, 1836 – May 10, 1901	Cambridge, Mass.
Apr. 1856	Torrey, Ebenezer	Aug. 16, 1801 – Sep. 15, 1888	Fitchburg, Mass.
Apr. 1973	Tourtellot, Arthur Bernon	Jul. 23, 1913 – Oct. 18, 1977	Westport, Conn.
Apr. 1963	Towner, Lawrence William	Sep. 10, 1921 –	Chicago, Ill.
Oct. 1908	Tozzer, Alfred Marston	Jul. 4, 1877 – Oct. 5, 1954	Cambridge, Mass.
Oct. 1983	Tranquada, Robert Ernest	Aug. 27, 1930 –	West Boylston, Mass.
Oct. 1915	Trevelyan, George Otto	Jul. 20, 1838 – Aug. 16, 1928	London, England
Oct. 1814	Trevett, Benjamin		New York, N.Y.
Oct. 1814	Trevett, Samuel Russell	Aug. 20, 1783 – Nov. 4, 1822	New York, N.Y.
Oct. 1814	Trumbull, Benjamin	Dec. 19, 1735 – Feb. 2, 1820	North Haven, Conn.
Apr. 1855	Trumbull, James Hammond	Dec. 20, 1821 – Aug. 5, 1897	Hartford, Conn.
Jul. 1815	Tucker, Ichabod	Apr. 17, 1765 – Oct. 22, 1846	Salem, Mass.
Apr. 1979	Tucker, Louis Leonard	Dec. 6, 1927 –	Boston, Mass.
Apr. 1894	*Tucker, William Jewett	Jul. 13, 1839 – Sep. 29, 1926	Hanover, N.H.
Apr. 1855	Tuckerman, Edward	Dec. 7, 1817 – May 15, 1886	Amherst, Mass.
Jun. 1814	Tudor, William	Mar. 28, 1750 – Jul. 8, 1819	Boston, Mass.
Oct. 1907	Turner, Frederick Jackson	Nov. 14, 1861 – Mar. 14, 1932	Madison, Wis.
Apr. 1908	Tuttle, Julius Herbert	Mar. 7, 1857 – Feb. 10, 1945	Dedham, Mass.

* resigned

Apr. 1970	Tweney, George Harrison	Sep. 16, 1915 –	Seattle, Wash.
Oct. 1986	Twigg-Smith, Thurston	Aug. 17, 1921 –	Honolulu, Hawaii
Oct. 1912	Tyler, Lyon Gardiner	Aug., 1853 – Feb. 12, 1935	Williamsburg, Va.
Apr. 1879	Tyler, Moses Coit	Aug. 2, 1835 – Dec. 28, 1900	Ann Arbor, Mich.
Apr. 1986	Tyler, Ronnie Curtis	Dec. 29, 1941 –	Austin, Tex.
Dec. 1813	Tyng, Dudley Atkins	Sep. 3, 1760 – Aug. 1, 1829	Cambridge, Mass.
Oct. 1904	Updike, Daniel Berkeley	Feb. 24, 1860 – Dec. 29, 1941	Boston, Mass.
Jul. 1815	Updike, Wilkins	Jan. 8, 1784 – Jan. 14, 1867	South Kingstown, R.I.
Oct. 1858	Upham, Charles Wentworth	May 4, 1802 – Jun. 15, 1875	Salem, Mass.
Oct. 1815	Upham, George Baxter	Dec. 27, 1768 – Feb. 10, 1848	Claremont, N.H.
Oct. 1893	Upham, Henry Pratt	Jan. 26, 1837 – May 1, 1909	St. Paul, Minn.
Apr. 1900	Utley, Samuel	Sep. 29, 1843 – Nov. 17, 1930	Worcester, Mass.
Oct. 1931	Vail, Robert William Glenroie	Mar. 26, 1890 – Jun. 21, 1966	Shrewsbury, Mass.
Apr. 1879	Valentini, Philipp Johann Joseph	1824 – Mar. 16, 1899	New York, N.Y.
Oct. 1822	Van Der Kemp, Francis Adrian	Mar. 4, 1752 – Sep. 7, 1829	New York, N.Y.
Oct. 1982	Vandiver, Frank Everson	Dec. 9, 1925 –	College Station, Tex.
Apr. 1942	Van Doren, Carl Clinton	Sep. 10, 1885 – Jul. 18, 1950	New York, N.Y.
Apr. 1963	Van Ravenswaay, Charles	Aug. 10, 1911 –	Sturbridge, Mass.
Jun. 1814	Van Rensselaer, Stephen	Nov. 1, 1764 – Jan. 26, 1839	Albany, N.Y.
Oct. 1922	Van Tyne, Claude Halstead	Oct. 16, 1869 – Mar. 21, 1930	Ann Arbor, Mich.
Oct. 1984	Varnum, Herbert Mason	Apr. 22, 1937 –	Paxton, Mass.
Dec. 1821	Vater, John Severin	1771 – Mar. 17, 1826	Halle, Germany
Apr. 1977	Vaughan, Alden True	Jan. 23, 1929 –	Cos Cob, Conn.
Dec. 1813	Vaughan, Benjamin	Apr. 30, 1751 – Dec. 8, 1835	Hallowell, Maine
May 1834	Vaux, Roberts	Jan. 21, 1786 – Jan. 7, 1836	Philadelphia, Pa.
Apr. 1901	Vedder, Charles Stuart	Oct. 7, 1826 – Mar. 2, 1917	Charleston, S.C.
Apr. 1893	Veragua, Duke of	1837 – Oct. 30, 1910	Madrid, Spain
Aug. 1820	Verplanck, Gulian Crommelin	Aug. 6, 1786 – Mar. 18, 1870	New York, N.Y.
Apr. 1972	Ver Steeg, Clarence Lester	Dec. 28, 1922 –	Evanston, Ill.
Jun. 1829	Vidaurre, Manuel Lorenzo	1773 – Mar. 9, 1841	Lima, Peru
Oct. 1963	Vietor, Alexander Orr	Nov. 13, 1913 – Mar. 9, 1981	New Haven, Conn.
Apr. 1942	Viets, Henry Rouse	Mar. 7, 1890 – Jul. 5, 1969	Boston, Mass.
Oct. 1896	Vignaud, Henry	Nov. 27, 1830 – Sep. 16, 1922	Paris, France
Apr. 1893	Vinogradoff, Paul	Dec. 1, 1854 – Dec. 19, 1925	Moscow, Russia

Apr. 1977	Vinovskis, Maris A.	Jan. 1, 1943 –	Ann Arbor, Mich.
Apr. 1903	Vinton, Alexander Hamilton	Mar. 30, 1852 – Jan. 18, 1911	Springfield, Mass.
Apr. 1868	Visconti, Pietro Ercole	ca. 1801 – Oct. 14, 1880	Rome, Italy
Oct. 1895	Vollgraff, Johann Christoph	Jan. 3, 1848 – Jan. 6, 1920	Brussels, Belgium
Oct. 1855	Vose, Richard Hampton	ca. 1863 – Jan. 19, 1864	Augusta, Maine
Oct. 1983	Waddel, Eugene Garland	Jun. 12, 1944 –	Charleston, S.C.
Apr. 1922	Wagner, Henry Raup	Sep. 27, 1862 – Mar. 28, 1957	Berkeley, Calif.
Apr. 1959	Wahlstrom, Carl Erhard	Jan. 27, 1898 – Dec. 11, 1974	Worcester, Mass.
Apr. 1960	Wainwright, Nicholas Biddle	Jul. 12, 1914 – Oct. 25, 1986	Philadelphia, Pa.
Apr. 1955	Waite, Albert Goodnow	Apr. 7, 1882 – Feb. 6, 1971	Worcester, Mass.
Oct. 1839	Waldeck, Jean Frederic De	Mar. 16, 1766 – May 2, 1875	London, England
Jul. 1826	Waldo, Daniel	Jan. 20, 1763 – Jul. 9, 1845	Worcester, Mass.
Oct. 1965	Walett, Francis Gustaf	Oct. 1, 1917 –	Westboro, Mass.
Oct. 1876	Walker, Francis Amasa	Jul. 2, 1840 – Jan. 5, 1897	New Haven, Conn.
Oct. 1954	Walker, Guy Warren, Jr.	Apr. 11, 1897 – Apr. 18, 1978	Beverly, Mass.
Apr. 1879	Walker, Joseph Burbeen	Jun. 12, 1822 – Jan. 8, 1913	Concord, N.H.
Apr. 1901	Walker, Williston	Jul. 1, 1860 – Mar. 9, 1922	New Haven, Conn.
Apr. 1924	Wall, Alexander James	Oct. 25, 1884 – Apr. 14, 1944	New York, N.Y.
Apr. 1956	Wall, Alexander James, Jr.	Sep. 12, 1912 –	Newark, N.J.
Apr. 1980	Wallace, Anthony Francis Clarke	Apr. 15, 1923 –	Philadelphia, Pa.
1812	Wallcut, Thomas	Aug. 16, 1758 – Jun. 5, 1840	Boston, Mass.
Apr. 1985	Walsh, John, Jr.	Dec. 9, 1937 –	Santa Monica, Calif.
Apr. 1959	Walsh, Michael Joseph	ca. 1893 – May 27, 1984	Boston, Mass.
Oct. 1865	Walworth, Reuben Hyde	Oct. 26, 1789 – Nov. 2, 1867	Saratoga, N.Y.
Apr. 1975	Ward, John William	Dec. 21, 1922 – Aug. 3, 1985	Amherst, Mass.
Jul. 1815	Ward, Samuel	Nov. 17, 1756 – Aug. 16, 1832	Greenwich, R.I.
Oct. 1813	Ward, Thomas Walter	Aug. 10, 1758 – Aug. 20, 1835	Shrewsbury, Mass.
Oct. 1924	Warner, Clarance Mac Donald	Mar. 31, 1874 – May 22, 1940	Boston, Mass.
Apr. 1965	Warner, Ezra Joseph, III	Jul. 4, 1910 – May 30, 1974	La Jolla, Calif.
Oct. 1981	Warner, Robert Mark	Jun. 28, 1927 –	Washington, D.C.
Oct. 1944	Warren, Charles	Mar. 9, 1868 – Aug. 16, 1954	Washington, D.C.
Oct. 1819	Warren, Henry	ca. 1764 – Jul. 3, 1828	Plymouth, Mass.
Apr. 1856	Warren, John Collins	Aug. 1, 1778 – May 4, 1856	Boston, Mass.
Apr. 1908	Washburn, Charles Grenfill	Jan. 28, 1857 – May 25, 1928	Worcester, Mass.
Oct. 1827	Washburn, Emory	Feb. 14, 1800 – Mar. 18, 1877	Leicester, Mass.
Apr. 1915	Washburn, Henry Bradford	Dec. 2, 1869 – Apr. 25, 1962	Cambridge, Mass.

Apr. 1882	Washburn, Israel	Jun. 6, 1813 – May 12, 1883	Portland, Maine
Apr. 1871	Washburn, John Davis	Mar. 28, 1833 – Apr. 4, 1903	Worcester, Mass.
Oct. 1930	Washburn, Reginald	Oct. 13, 1871 – May 12, 1955	Worcester, Mass.
Apr. 1969	Washburn, Wilcomb Edward	Jan. 13, 1925 –	Washington, D.C.
Dec. 1813	Washington, Bushrod	Jun. 5, 1762 – Nov. 26, 1829	Mount Vernon, Va.
Oct. 1901	Waters, Thomas Franklin	Apr. 12, 1851 – Nov. 23, 1919	Ipswich, Mass.
Apr. 1871	Waterston, Robert Cassie	Mar. 20, 1812 – Feb. 21, 1893	Boston, Mass.
Jul. 1815	Watson, Elkanah	Jan. 22, 1758 – Dec. 5, 1842	Pittsfield, Mass.
Jun. 1814	Watt, James T. B.		Jamaica, West Indies
Oct. 1851	Wayland, Francis	Mar. 11, 1796 – Sep. 30, 1865	Providence, R.I.
Apr. 1981	Weaver, Glenn	May 28, 1917 –	Hartford, Conn.
Oct. 1814	Webster, Daniel	Jan. 18, 1782 – Oct. 24, 1852	Portsmouth, N.H.
1812	Webster, Redford	ca. 1761 – Aug. 31, 1833	Boston, Mass.
Oct. 1944	Wecter, Dixon	Jan. 12, 1906 – Jun. 24, 1950	Los Angeles, Calif.
Oct. 1947	Weddell, Alexander Wilbourne	Apr. 6, 1876 – Jan. 1, 1948	Richmond, Va.
Apr. 1981	Wedgeworth, Robert	Jul. 31, 1937 –	Chicago, Ill.
Apr. 1884	Weeden, William Babcock	Sep. 1, 1834 – Mar. 28, 1912	Providence, R.I.
Oct. 1979	Weins, Leo Matthew	Sep. 2, 1912 –	New York, N.Y.
Oct. 1982	Weir, Robert Mc Colloch	Aug. 26, 1933 –	Columbia, S.C.
Oct. 1938	Weis, Frederick Lewis	Aug. 22, 1895 – Apr. 11, 1966	Lancaster, Mass.
Apr. 1980	Weissman, Stephen David	Dec. 25, 1938 –	New York, N.Y.
Apr. 1955	Welch, James d'Alté Aldridge	Apr. 9, 1907 – Jan. 4, 1970	Cleveland, Ohio
Oct. 1928	Welles, Lemuel Aikin	Nov., 1870 – Feb. 15, 1953	New York, N.Y.
Oct. 1943	Wells, Albert Bacheller	Nov. 19, 1872 – Mar. 10, 1953	Southbridge, Mass.
Oct. 1977	Wells, James M.	Nov. 4, 1917 –	Chicago, Ill.
Oct. 1948	Wells, Joel Cheney	Nov. 11, 1874 – Jan. 6, 1960	Southbridge, Mass.
Apr. 1974	*Wells, Ruth Dyer		Charlton City, Mass.
Oct. 1840	Wells, Samuel	Dec. 21, 1792 – Oct. 4, 1864	Northampton, Mass.
1812	Wells, William	Apr. 27, 1773 – Apr. 21, 1860	Boston, Mass.
Oct. 1976	Welter, Rush Eastman	Sep. 28, 1923 –	North Pownal, Vt.
Apr. 1910	Wendell, Barrett	Aug. 23, 1855 – Feb. 8, 1921	Boston, Mass.
Apr. 1946	Wertenbaker, Thomas Jefferson	Feb. 6, 1879 – Apr. 22, 1966	Princeton, N.J.
Apr. 1981	Wesby, Meridith Daniels	May 31, 1943 –	Holden, Mass.

* resigned

Apr. 1977	Wesley, Charles Harris	Dec. 2, 1891 – Aug. 16, 1987	Washington, D.C.
Oct. 1962	Wessen, Ernest James	Dec. 4, 1887 – Dec. 13, 1974	Mansfield, Ohio
Oct. 1950	Wheat, Carl Irving	Dec. 5, 1892 – Jun. 23, 1966	Washington, D.C.
Apr. 1871	Wheatland, Henry	Jan. 11, 1812 – Feb. 27, 1893	Salem, Mass.
Oct. 1820	Wheaton, Henry	Nov. 27, 1785 – Mar. 11, 1848	New York, N.Y.
Apr. 1915	Wheeler, Leonard	Aug. 3, 1845 – Oct. 2, 1935	Worcester, Mass.
Apr. 1956	Wheeler, Nathaniel	Jun. 20, 1906 – Mar. 14, 1979	Worcester, Mass.
Aug. 1820	Wheeler, Theophilus	ca. 1764 – Aug. 14, 1840	Worcester, Mass.
Jun. 1813	Wheelock, John	Jan. 28, 1754 – Apr. 4, 1817	Hanover, N.H.
Apr. 1894	Whipple, Henry Benjamin	Feb. 15, 1823 – 1901	Faribault, Minn.
Oct. 1884	White, Andrew Dickson	Nov. 7, 1832 – Nov. 4, 1918	Ithaca, N.Y.
Oct. 1976	White, Morton Gabriel	Apr. 29, 1917 –	Princeton, N.J.
Oct. 1855	Whitehead, William Adee	Feb. 19, 1810 – Aug. 8, 1884	Newark, N.J.
Apr. 1942	Whitehill, Walter Muir	Sep. 28, 1905 – Mar. 5, 1978	Salem, Mass.
Apr. 1910	Whitin, Albert Henry	Jun. 22, 1853 – Mar. 6, 1935	Whitinsville, Mass.
Jun. 1814	Whitman, Isaac Winslow	Sep. 13, 1789 – Mar. 14, 1831	Brewster, Mass.
Jun. 1814	Whitman, Jonas	May 18, 1749 – Jul. 30, 1824	Barnstable, Mass.
Jun. 1814	Whitman, Kilborn	Aug. 17, 1765 – Dec. 11, 1835	Pembroke, Mass.
Oct. 1894	Whitney, James Lyman	Nov. 28, 1835 – Sep. 25, 1910	Cambridge, Mass.
Apr. 1868	Whitney, William Dwight	Feb. 9, 1827 – Jun. 7, 1894	New Haven, Conn.
Apr. 1870	Whittlesey, Charles	Oct. 5, 1808 – Oct. 18, 1886	Cleveland, Ohio
Apr. 1963	Wiggins, James Russell	Dec. 4, 1903 –	Washington, D.C.
Apr. 1920	Wilbur, James Benjamin	Nov. 11, 1856 – Apr. 28, 1929	Manchester, Vt.
Oct. 1816	Wilkins, Charles		Lexington, Ky.
Oct. 1947	Wilkins, Raymond Sanger	May 24, 1891 – May 12, 1971	Salem, Mass.
Sep. 1813	Wilkinson, William	Mar. 19, 1760 – May 16, 1852	Providence, R.I.
Jul. 1826	Willard, Joseph	Mar. 14, 1798 – May 12, 1865	Lancaster, Mass.
Sep. 1813	Willard, Samuel	Apr. 18, 1775 – Oct. 8, 1859	Deerfield, Mass.
Jun. 1813	Willard, Sidney	Sep. 19, 1780 – Dec. 6, 1856	Cambridge, Mass.
Oct. 1983	Willcox, William Bradford	Oct. 29, 1907 – Sep. 15, 1985	New Haven, Conn.
May 1838	Williams, John Bickerton	Mar. 4, 1792 – Oct. 21, 1855	Shrewsbury, England
Apr. 1882	Williams, John Fletcher	Sep. 25, 1834 – Apr. 29, 1895	St. Paul, Minn.
Oct. 1981	Williams, Peter Howard Creagh	Mar. 15, 1935 –	North Grafton, Mass.
Apr. 1978	Williams, Richmond Dean	Dec. 10, 1925 –	Greenville, Del.
Oct. 1819	Williams, Samuel	Oct. 16, 1786 – Feb. 3, 1859	Cincinnati, Ohio
Jan. 1819	Williams, Samuel	Feb. 23, 1788 – Sep. 19, 1853	London, England
Apr. 1944	Williams, Stanley Thomas	Oct. 25, 1888 – May 5, 1956	New Haven, Conn.

Jan. 1819	Williams, Stephen	ca. 1772 – Feb. 6, 1838	Northborough, Mass.
Oct. 1819	Williams, Thomas	ca. 1765 – Sep. 20, 1823	Roxbury, Mass.
1812	Williams, Timothy	ca. 1766 – Feb. 19, 1846	Boston, Mass.
Dec. 1813	Williamson, Hugh	Dec. 5, 1735 – May 22, 1819	New York, N.Y.
Oct. 1897	Williamson, Joseph	Oct. 5, 1828 – Dec. 4, 1902	Belfast, Maine
Apr. 1864	Willis, William	Aug. 31, 1794 – Feb. 17, 1870	Portland, Maine
Apr. 1978	Wilmerding, John	Apr. 28, 1938 –	Washington, D.C.
Apr. 1938	Wilmerding, Lucius	Jan. 24, 1880 – Jul. 15, 1949	New York, N.Y.
Apr. 1942	Wilson, Carroll Atwood	May 12, 1886 – Jun. 27, 1947	New York, N.Y.
Apr. 1861	Wilson, Daniel	Jan. 5, 1826 – Aug. 6, 1892	Toronto, Ont.
Oct. 1816	Wilson, James		Philadelphia, Pa.
Apr. 1868	Wilson, John Newman	Nov. 21, 1802 – Oct. 8, 1872	Newark, Ohio
Jul. 1815	Wilson, Joshua Lacey	Sep. 22, 1774 – Aug. 14, 1846	Cincinnati, Ohio
Jul. 1815	Wilson, Robert G.	d. Apr. 17, 1851	Chillicothe, Ohio
Oct. 1936	Wilson, Samuel Mackay	Oct. 15, 1871 – Oct. 10, 1946	Lexington, Ky.
Apr. 1818	Wilson, William	Mar. 19, 1773 – Jun. 6, 1827	Newark, Ohio
Oct. 1913	Wilson, Woodrow	Dec. 28, 1856 – Feb. 3, 1924	Washington, D.C.
Oct. 1979	Winkworth, Peter	Apr. 25, 1929 –	London, England
Apr. 1899	Winship, George Parker	Jul. 29, 1871 – Jun. 22, 1952	Providence, R.I.
Apr. 1986	Winship, Michael	Dec. 16, 1950 –	Cambridge, Mass.
Jun. 1814	Winslow, Isaac	Apr. 27, 1739 – Oct. 24, 1819	Marshfield, Mass.
Jun. 1814	Winslow, John	Oct. 29, 1753 – Nov. 29, 1819	Hanover, Mass.
Oct. 1880	Winsor, Justin	Jan. 2, 1831 – Oct. 22, 1897	Cambridge, Mass.
Apr. 1984	Winston, Michael Russell	May 26, 1941 –	Washington, D.C.
Jul. 1826	Winthrop, Adam	d. 1846	Baton Rouge, La.
Oct. 1924	Winthrop, Frederic	Nov. 15, 1868 – May 6, 1932	Boston, Mass.
Jun. 1813	Winthrop, James	Mar. 28, 1752 – Sep. 26, 1821	Cambridge, Mass.
Oct. 1838	Winthrop, Robert Charles	May 12, 1809 – Nov. 16, 1894	Boston, Mass.
Oct. 1894	Winthrop, Robert Charles, Jr.	Dec. 7, 1834 – Jun. 5, 1905	Boston, Mass.
Jun. 1813	Winthrop, Thomas Lindall	Mar. 6, 1760 – Feb. 22, 1841	Boston, Mass.
Apr. 1890	Winthrop, Thomas Lindall	Aug. 16, 1835 – Dec. 6, 1920	Boston, Mass.
Oct. 1813	Winthrop, William	Apr. 19, 1753 – Feb. 5, 1825	Cambridge, Mass.
Jun. 1814	Wolcott, Oliver	Jan. 11, 1760 – Jun. 1, 1833	Hartford, Conn.
Apr. 1944	Wolcott, Roger	Jul. 25, 1877 – Apr. 21, 1965	Milton, Mass.
Oct. 1953	Wolf, Edwin, II	Dec. 6, 1911 –	Philadelphia, Pa.
Oct. 1966	Wolfe, Richard James	May 7, 1928 –	Boston, Mass.
Apr. 1934	Wolkins, George Gregerson	May 2, 1878 – Mar. 2, 1951	Boston, Mass.

Apr. 1976	Wood, Gordon Stewart	Nov. 27, 1933 –	Barrington, R.I.
Apr. 1984	Wood, Osgood Bradley	Aug. 13, 1918 –	Worcester, Mass.
Oct. 1979	Wood, Peter Hutchins	May 1, 1943 –	Durham, N.C.
Apr. 1976	Wood, Robert Coldwell	Sep. 16, 1923 –	Lincoln, Mass.
Apr. 1910	Wood, William Charles Henry	d. Sep. 2, 1947	Quebec, Que.
Apr. 1918	Woodbury, John	Jan. 26, 1856 – Jan. 4, 1940	Boston, Mass
Apr. 1983	Woodbury, John Clark	Jun. 10, 1929 –	Worcester, Mass.
Oct. 1907	Woods, Henry Ernest	Jun. 5, 1857 – Oct. 11, 1919	Boston, Mass.
May 1845	Woods, Leonard	Nov. 24, 1807 – Dec. 24, 1878	Brunswick, Maine
Apr. 1864	Woodward, Ashbel	Jun. 26, 1804 – Dec. 20, 1885	Franklin, Conn.
Oct. 1976	Woodward, Comer Vann	Nov. 13, 1908 –	Hamden, Conn.
Oct. 1980	Woodward, Harold Edward	Jul. 5, 1888 –	Worcester, Mass.
Oct. 1985	Woodward, Robert C.	May 26, 1924 –	Bangor, Maine
Oct. 1865	Woodward, Rufus	Oct. 3, 1819 – Dec. 30, 1885	Worcester, Mass.
May 1841	Woodward, Samuel Bayard	Jan. 10, 1787 – Jan. 3, 1850	Worcester, Mass.
Apr. 1908	Woodward, Samuel Bayard	Aug. 24, 1853 – Jan. 29, 1946	Worcester, Mass.
Jul. 1815	Woolley, Abram		Pittsburgh, Pa.
Oct. 1926	Woolsey, John Munro	Jan. 3, 1877 – May 4, 1945	New York, N.Y.
Apr. 1978	Woolsey, John Munro, Jr.	Apr. 22, 1916 –	Cambridge, Mass.
Apr. 1970	Wormser, Richard Samuel	Apr. 5, 1898 – Apr. 6, 1975	Bethel, Conn.
Apr. 1893	Wright, Carroll Davidson	Jul. 25, 1840 – Feb. 20, 1909	Reading, Mass.
Apr. 1939	Wright, Harry Andrew	Jun. 30, 1872 – Oct. 20, 1950	Springfield, Mass.
Jul. 1815	Wright, John		New Lancaster, Ohio
Oct. 1975	Wright, John Cardinal	Jul. 18, 1909 – Aug. 10, 1979	Rome, Italy
Oct. 1947	Wright, Louis Booker	Mar. 1, 1899 – Feb. 26, 1984	San Marino, Calif.
Oct. 1953	Wright, Lyle Henry	Nov. 6, 1903 – Nov. 24, 1979	San Marino, Calif.
Oct. 1910	Wrong, George McKinnon	Jun. 25, 1860 – Jun. 29, 1948	Toronto, Ont.
Apr. 1923	Wroth, Lawrence Counselman	Jan. 14, 1884-Dec. 25, 1970	Baltimore, Md.
Jul. 1815	Wylie, Andrew	Apr. 12, 1789 – Nov. 11, 1851	Canonsburg, Pa.
Oct. 1948	Wyllie, John Cook	Oct. 26, 1908 – Apr. 18, 1968	Charlottesville, Va.
Apr. 1868	Wyman, Jeffries	Aug. 11, 1814 – Sep. 5, 1874	Cambridge, Mass.
Oct. 1873	Wynne, Thomas Hicks	Jan. 22, 1820 – Feb. 24, 1875	Richmond, Va.
Oct. 1882	Ximenes De La Espada, Marcos		Madrid, Spain
May 1841	Young, Alexander	Sep. 22, 1800 – Mar. 16, 1854	Boston, Mass.
Oct. 1981	Young, Alfred Fabian	Jan. 17, 1925 –	Oak Park, Ill.
Oct. 1968	*Young, George Berkeley	Jul. 27, 1913 –	Chicago, Ill.

* resigned

Oct. 1983	Young, Mary Elizabeth	Dec. 16, 1929–	Rochester, N.Y.
Apr. 1940	Zabriskie, George Albert	Dec. 7, 1868 – Feb. 2, 1954	New York, N.Y.
Oct. 1882	Zaragoza, Justo		Madrid, Spain
Apr. 1976	Zeitlin, Jacob	Nov. 4, 1902 – Aug. 31, 1987	Los Angeles, Calif.
Oct. 1979	Ziff, Larzer	Oct. 2, 1927–	Philadelphia, Pa.
Oct. 1985	Zinman, Michael	Mar. 4, 1932–	Ardsley, N.Y.
Oct. 1967	Zobel, Hiller Bellin	Feb. 23, 1932–	Lexington, Mass.

Officers of the Society, 1812–1987

PRESIDENTS

1812–1831	Isaiah Thomas	1929–1933	Calvin Coolidge
1831–1841	Thomas Lindall Winthrop	1933–1938	Arthur Prentice Rugg
1841–1853	Edward Everett	1938–1952	Samuel Eliot Morison
1853–1854	John Davis	1952–1955	Thomas Winthrop Streeter
1854–1884	Stephen Salisbury	1955–1959	Clarence Saunders Brigham
1884–1887	George Frisbie Hoar	1959–1964	Carleton Rubira Richmond
1887–1905	Stephen Salisbury, Jr.	1964–1970	Clifton Waller Barrett
1906–1907	Edward Everett Hale	1970–1977	James Russell Wiggins
1907–1927	Waldo Lincoln	1977–	John Jeppson, 2nd
1927–1929	Charles Lemuel Nichols		

VICE-PRESIDENTS

1812–1816	William Dandridge Peck	1887–1904	George Frisbee Hoar
1813–1816	William Paine	1891–1906	Edward Everett Hale
1816–1831	Aaron Bancroft	1904–1918	Samuel Abbott Green
1816–1821	Timothy Bigelow	1906–1907	Waldo Lincoln
1821–1828	DeWitt Clinton	1907–1909	Edward Everett Hale
1828–1831	Thomas Lindall Winthrop	1909–1920	Andrew McFarland Davis
1831–1853	John Davis	1919–1933	Arthur Prentice Rugg
1831–1845	Joseph Story	1920–1935	Clarence Winthrop Bowen
1846–1853	William Buell Sprague	1933–1940	Charles Henry Taylor
1853–1866	William Jenks	1936–1942	William Vail Kellen
1853–1854	Stephen Salisbury	1940–1950	Paul Beagary Morgan
1854–1868	Levi Lincoln	1943–1964	George Sumner Barton
1867–1878	Benjamin Franklin Thomas	1950–1952	Thomas Winthrop Streeter
1868–1880	James Lenox	1952–1954	George Hubbard Blakeslee
1878–1884	George Frisbie Hoar	1954–1959	Carleton Rubira Richmond
1880–1891	George Bancroft	1959–1964	Clifton Waller Barrett
1884–1887	Stephen Salisbury, Jr.	1964–1969	John Jeppson, 2nd

1965–1972 Alden Porter Johnson
1969–1970 James Russell Wiggins
1970–1971 John William Middendorf
1971–1973 Keyes Dewitt Metcalf
1972–1979 Bernard Bailyn
1973–1977 John Jeppson, 2nd
1978– Roderick Douglas Stinehour
1979–1985 John William Ward
1985– Jill Kathryn Ker Conway

TREASURERS

1813–1813 Levi Lincoln, Jr.
1813–1819 Isaiah Thomas, Jr.
1819–1829 Nathaniel Maccarty
1829–1843 Samuel Jennison
1843–1846 Alfred Dwight Foster
1846–1860 Samuel Jennison
1860–1863 Henry Chapin
1863–1907 Nathaniel Paine
1907–1916 Augustus George Bullock
1916–1927 Samuel Bayard Woodward
1927–1961 Chandler Bullock
1961–1972 Augustus George Bullock
1972– Bruce Goddard Daniels

RECORDING SECRETARIES

1812–1814 Samuel Macgregor Burnside
1814–1815 Oliver Fiske
1815–1854 Rejoice Newton
1854–1858 Edward Everett Hale
1858–1861 Alexander Hamilton Bullock
1861–1865 Edward Mellen
1865–1871 Alonzo Hill
1871–1894 John Davis Washburn
1894–1906 Charles Augustus Chase
1906–1909 Andrew McFarland Davis
1909–1913 George Parker Winship
1913–1921 Charles Lemuel Nichols
1921–1938 Thomas Hovey Gage
1938–1946 George Hubbard Blakeslee
1946–1967 Daniel Waldo Lincoln
1967– Linwood Mandeville Erskine, Jr.

CORRESPONDING SECRETARIES

1812–1831 Thaddeus Mason Harris
1813–1816 William Jenks
1814–1823 Samuel MacGregor Burnside
1816–1828 Abiel Holmes
1820–1821 Samuel Jennison
1823–1826 Samuel Jennison
1826–1831 William Lincoln

SECRETARIES FOR DOMESTIC CORRESPONDENCE

1831–1841	William Lincoln
1841–1867	Benjamin Franklin Thomas
1867–1877	Emory Washburn
1877–1880	George Bancroft
1880–1889	Charles Deane
1890–1894	George Edward Ellis
1895–1915	Charles Francis Adams
1915–1929	Worthington Chauncey Ford
1929–1938	Clarence Saunders Brigham
1958–1967	Clifford Kenyon Shipton
1967–1969	Marcus Allen McCorison
1969–1973	Clifford Kenyon Shipton
1974–1978	Walter Muir Whitehill
1978–1981	Robert Bruce Hitchman
1981–	Philip Charles Beals

SECRETARIES FOR FOREIGN CORRESPONDENCE

1831–1832	Thaddeus Mason Harris
1832–1841	Edward Everett
1840–1846	John Pickering
1846–1866	Jared Sparks
1866–1867	Emory Washburn
1867–1874	Charles Sumner
1874–1897	J. Hammond Trumbull
1897–1912	Franklin Bowditch Dexter
1912–1921	James Phinney Baxter
1921–1927	Charles Lemuel Nichols
1927–1938	George Hubbard Blakeslee
1958–1965	Alden Porter Johnson
1965–1970	Richard Allen Heald
1970–1974	Frank Leighton Harrington
1974–1977	Keyes Dewitt Metcalf
1977–1979	Robert Waring Stoddard
1979–	Henry Schofield Streeter

SECRETARY FOR FOREIGN AND DOMESTIC CORRESPONDENCE

1938–1958	Clarence Saunders Brigham

DIRECTORS

1930–1959	Clarence Saunders Brigham
1959–1967	Clifford Kenyon Shipton
1967–	Marcus Allen McCorison

LIBRARIANS

1814–1826	Samuel Jennison
1826–1827	William Lincoln
1827–1830	Christopher Columbus Baldwin
1830–1831	Samuel MacGregor Burnside
1832–1835	Christopher Columbus Baldwin
1835–1838	Maturin Lewis Fisher
1838–1881	Samuel Foster Haven
1883–1908	Edmund Mills Barton
1908–1930	Clarence Saunders Brigham
1930–1940	Robert William Glenroie Vail
1940–1960	Clifford Kenyon Shipton
1960–	Marcus Allen McCorison

COUNCILLORS

1813–1816	Timothy Bigelow
1813–1816	Aaron Bancroft
1813–1818	Edward Bangs
1813–1814	George Gibbs
1813–1819	William Bentley
1813–1816	Redford Webster
1813–1845	Benjamin Russell
1814–1819	Samuel Jackson Prescott
1815–1816	William Stedman
1815–1826	Oliver Fiske
1815–1820	Nathaniel Paine
1815–1819	George Thacher
1815–1820	Kilborn Whitman
1816–1830	Edward Hutchinson Robbins
1816–1817	Francis Blake
1816–1821	James Winthrop
1816–1817	Levi Lincoln
1817–1854	Levi Lincoln, Jr.
1817–1828	Abijah Bigelow
1819–1821	Mark Langdon Hill
1819–1831	William Jenks
1820–1853	Charles Lowell
1820–1823	Samuel Jennison
1820–1824	Edward Dillingham Bangs
1820–1821	Joshua Thomas
1821–1828	Thomas Lindall Winthrop
1823–1850	Samuel MacGregor Burnside
1824–1831	John Davis
1826–1832	Isaac Goodwin
1828–1830	Samuel Jennison
1828–1852	James Cushing Merrill
1830–1853	Frederick William Paine
1831–1833	James Bowdoin
1831–1838	Edward Dillingham Bangs
1831–1855	John Green
1832–1842	John Park
1833–1853	Joseph Willard
1838–1856	Emory Washburn
1842–1843	Benjamin Franklin Thomas
1843–1853	Stephen Salisbury
1845–1846	Samuel Jennison
1846–1852	Alfred Dwight Foster
1850–1883	Isaac Davis
1852–1854	Edward Everett Hale
1852–1853	Charles Sumner
1853–1865	George Livermore
1853–1874	Nathaniel Bradstreet Shurtleff
1853–1872	Charles Folsom
1853–1867	Ira Moore Barton
1853–1858	Thomas Kinnicutt
1854–1867	Pliny Merrick
1854–1868	John Prescott Bigelow
1855–1881	Samuel Foster Haven
1856–1863	Dwight Foster
1858–1891	Edward Everett Hale
1863–1888	Joseph Sargent

1865–1880 Charles Deane
1867–1878 Seth Sweetser
1867–1880 Richard Frothingham
1868–1878 Henry Chapin
1872–1874 J. Hammond Trumbull
1874–1904 Samuel Abbott Green
1874–1884 Stephen Salisbury, Jr.
1878–1895 Peleg Emory Aldrich
1878–1885 Edward Henry Hall
1880–1904 Egbert Coffin Smyth
1880–1884 Dwight Foster
1881–1882 Alexander Hamilton Bullock
1882–1884 William Reed Huntington
1883–1918 Samuel Swett Green
1884–1893 Andrew Preston Peabody
1884–1894 Charles Augustus Chase
1884–1912 Edward Livingston Davis
1885–1897 Franklin Bowditch Dexter
1888–1902 Jeremiah Evarts Greene
1891–1921 Granville Stanley Hall
1893–1912 William Babcock Weeden
1894–1903 John Davis Washburn
1895–1901 Thomas Corwin Mendenhall
1897–1912 James Phinney Baxter
1901–1903 Henry Stedman Nourse
1903–1909 Carroll Davidson Wright
1903–1911 Edmund Arthur Engler
1904–1906 Andrew McFarland Davis
1904–1909 Elias Harlow Russell
1904–1925 Samuel Utley
1906–1911 Charles Augustus Chase
1907–1917 Nathaniel Paine
1909–1919 Arthur Prentice Rugg
1911–1928 Charles Grenfill Washburn
1911–1913 Charles Lemuel Nichols
1912–1933 Francis Henshaw Dewey
1912–1930 Henry Winchester Cunningham
1912–1920 Clarence Winthrop Bowen
1913–1952 George Parker Winship
1917–1930 William Howard Taft
1918–1927 George Hubbard Blakeslee
1919–1922 Henry Herbert Edes
1920–1929 Clarence Saunders Brigham
1921–1929 James Benjamin Wilbur
1922–1930 Samuel Lyman Munson
1925–1936 William Vail Kellen
1927–1933 Waldo Lincoln
1929–1940 Paul Beagary Morgan
1929–1933 Charles Henry Taylor
1929–1940 William Evarts Benjamin
1930–1943 George Sumner Barton
1930–1948 Aldus Chapin Higgins
1931–1940 Matt Bushnell Jones
1933–1938 Homer Gage
1933–1938 Francis Russell Hart
1936–1954 James Melville Hunnewell
1938–1946 Daniel Waldo Lincoln
1938–1959 Russell Sturgis Paine
1938–1965 Albert White Rice
1940–1941 Charles Henry Taylor, Jr.
1940–1958 Donald McKay Frost
1940–1942 John Hinsdale Scheide
1941–1951 Augustus Peabody Loring, Jr.
1942–1950 Thomas Winthrop Streeter
1943–1955 Stephen Willard Phillips
1946–1952 George Hubbard Blakeslee
1948–1965 Richard Allen Heald
1950–1952 Paul Beagary Morgan
1951–1954 Carleton Rubira Richmond
1952–1968 Edward Larocque Tinker
1952–1974 Walter Muir Whitehill
1953–1964 Harry Galpin Stoddard
1954–1961 Augustus George Bullock
1954–1971 Keyes De Witt Metcalf
1955–1965 Thomas Winthrop Streeter
1958–1959 Clifton Waller Barrett
1959–1963 Clarence Saunders Brigham
1959–1967 Fred Harold Daniels
1961–1962 Chandler Bullock

1963–1970 Frank Leighton Harrington
1963–1964 John Jeppson, 2nd
1964–1970 Carleton Rubira Richmond
1964–1973 Paris Fletcher
1965–1967 Linwood Mandeville Erskine
1965–1977 Robert Waring Stoddard
1965–1967 Marcus Allen McCorison
1967–1971 Daniel Waldo Lincoln
1967–1969 Clifford Kenyon Shipton
1967–1969 James Russell Wiggins
1968–1975 Bertram Wallace Korn
1969–1973 John Jeppson, 2nd
1969–1970 John William Middendorf
1969–1972 Bernard Bailyn
1970–1977 Clifton Waller Barrett
1970–1977 Everett Lee De Golyer, Jr.
1970–1978 Robert Bruce Hitchman
1971–1976 William Howard Adams
1971–1981 Howard Bonar Jefferson
1971–1979 Henry Schofield Streeter
1972–1980 Henry Bowen Dewey
1973–1983 Keyes DeWitt Metcalf
1973–1981 Philip Charles Beals
1973–1979 Cecelia Marie Kenyon
1974– Richard Charles Steele
1974– George Thomas Tanselle
1974–1977 Arthur Bernon Tourtellot
1975–1981 Walter Douglas Bell
1975– William Henry Bond
1976–1978 Roderick Douglas Stinehour
1977–1983 James Russell Wiggins
1977– Jules David Prown
1977–1985 John William Ward
1978–1983 Jack Phillip Greene
1978–1984 James Robert Maguire
1978–1982 Leonard Benjamin Schlosser
1979–1984 Homer Daniels Babbidge, Jr.
1979–1985 Jill Kathryn Ker Conway
1979– Robert Cushman
1980– Harold Taylor Miller
1981– Robert Palmer Hallock, Jr.
1981– Jacob Hiatt
1981–1986 Kenneth Nebenzahl
1983– Julian Lee Lapides
1983– Pauline Rubbelke Maier
1983– David Frederick Tatham
1984–1985 Betsey Beinecke Shirley
1984– John Munro Woolsey, Jr.
1985– James Robert Maguire
1985– Betty Ruth Ring
1986– Barbara Welch Sudler

Staff of the Society, 1986–1987

1980 Abbott, Carroll M., receptionist

1953 Adams, Eleanor S., executive assistant to the director

1984 Adams, Kevin F., assistant in buildings and grounds

1971 Allen, Carolyn A., acquisitions administrator

1968 Anders, Richard L., cataloguer

1980 Arbour, Keith, head of readers' services

1982 Baker, Richard C., chief book and paper conservator

1968 Barnhill, Georgia B., Andrew W. Mellon curator of graphic arts

1965 Beaudette, Dorothy M., assistant cataloguer

1982 Bengtson, Marie T., assistant in the Development Office

1984 Bernard, Frances G., accountant

1984 Biegay, Paula A., assistant cataloguer in the North American Imprints Program

1986 Blaine, Jacqueline M., archives assistant

1987 Bouphavichith, Souksavanh, clerical assistant

1987 Budwig, Judith H., conservation intern

1973 Burkett, Nancy H., assistant librarian

1976 Callahan, Mary V. C., development officer

1981 Chaison, Joanne D., head of readers' services

1977 Degutis, Alan N., head of cataloguing services

1954 Desautels, Kenneth R., conservation technician

1986 DiPilla, Gino, assistant in buildings and grounds

1967 Donoghue, Margaret A., assistant cataloguer in the North American Imprints Program

1978 Dunbar, Bradford F., receptionist

1981 Fyffe, Richard C., senior cataloguer in the American Children's Books Cataloguing Project

1982 Gordon, Susan J. W., cataloguer in the American Children's Books Cataloguing Project

1982 Gunnarson, Martha, co-supervisor in the Newspaper Cataloguing Project

1984 Hall, David D., chairman of the Program in the History of the Book in American Culture

1973 Hench, John B., associate director for research and publication

1979 Hosmer, Herbert H., honorary consultant on children's literature

1986 Joyce, William D., substitute librarian

1974 Kanis, Carol R., cataloguing specialist for authority work
1976 Lamoureux, Marie E., genealogy specialist in readers' services
1978 Laurie, Dennis R., assistant in newspapers
1983 McAvey, M. Sheila, assistant editor
1960 McCorison, Marcus A., director and librarian
1987 Magnuson, Lorry W., acquisitions clerk
1983 Meitzler, Pamela F., cataloguer in the North American Imprints Program
1982 Moore, Anne C., cataloguer in the North American Imprints Program
1987 Neale, Jane P., assistant in graphic arts
1986 Nicholson, Anne V., clerical assistant in the North American Imprints Program
1979 O'Keefe, Doris N., senior cataloguer
1978 Patterson, Carol-Ann, secretary to the director
1977 Pingeton, Joan M., acquisitions assistant
1986 Poisson, Marie-Therese J., assistant in readers' services
1982 Prendiville, Linda M., housekeeper
1980 Purcell, James J., receptionist
1984 Rapp, Ann-Cathrine, events coordinator
1984 Rugh, C. Dianne, assistant cataloguing specialist for authority work
1985 St. John, Peggy M., clerical assistant
1985 Savage, Sean J., assistant in readers' services
1981 Schoen, Diane B., secretary in research and publication
1987 Shepardson, Gayle S., assistant in readers' services
1984 Simmons, Barbara Trippel, curator of manuscripts
1972 Strader, Donald K., superintendent of buildings and grounds
1983 Tosi, Ernest A., receptionist
1973 Tracy, Joyce A., curator of newspapers and serials
1987 Wasowicz, Laura E., senior cataloguer in the American Children's Books Cataloguing Project
1973 Zook, Audrey T., assistant in serials